EOGRAPHY

Global climate change

Alastair Dawson

D UNIVERSITY PRESS

ACKNOWLEDGEMENTS

The publishers and author would like to thank the following people for their permission to use copyright material:

Photos: p.4 Frank Spooner Pictures, Photo News/Gamma; p.14 John Sanford, Science Photo Library; p.17 Magnum Photos; p.24 Prof. Stewart Lowther, Science Photo Library; p.26 Luigi Tazzari, Frank Spooner Pictures, Gamma; p.31 *top* Dr B. Booth, GSF Picture Library, *middle* Bruce Iverson, Science Photo Library, *bottom* Peter Ryan, Science Photo Library; p.39 Museum of London; p.41 Tom Zimberoff, Frank Spooner Pictures, Gamma.

Illustrations: p.6 John Wiley & Sons; p.13 C.E. Merrell Publishing Co.; p.16 New Scientist; p.21 John Wiley & Sons; p.23 Methuen & Co. Ltd.; p.27 *a* New Scientist, *b,c* R.A. Warrick; p.29 John Wiley & Sons, Oxford University Press; p.35 H.P. Sejrup; p.37 John Wiley & Sons; p.38 Methuen & Co. Ltd.; p.41 C.E. Merrell Publishing Co.; p.44 New Scientist.

The cover photograph is reproduced by permission of Eric Bouvet, Frank Spooner Pictures/Gamma.

Illustrations are by Herb Bowes Graphics, Oxford.

Every effort has been made to trace and contact copyright holders, but this has not always been possible. We apologise for any infringement of copyright.

PREFACE

Contemporary Issues in Geography is a series of books dealing with issues of concern to today's society. The series was developed as a result of our own teaching needs, especially when preparing INSET courses for teachers in Coventry and Warwickshire.

Hugh Matthews and Ian Foster, Series Editors

This book

Ten years ago, concern was expressed about the possibility that the earth would soon enter another Ice Age. Today, interest has shifted away from concerns about future global overcooling. Instead, attention is being focused upon the imminent threat of global warming. This change in emphasis has largely been due to the remarkable warmth that characterised the 1980s. There have been many suggestions put forward to account for this warming. These include the enhanced 'greenhouse effect' caused by a build-up of carbon dioxide in the earth's atmosphere. Another view is that recent global warming has been due to a marked increase in the sun's activity.

This book examines the evidence for climate change, assesses the factors involved, and looks at the likely environmental impacts of future changes.

Alastair Dawson

Typeset by Gem Publishing Company, Wallingford
Design and artwork by Herb Bowes Graphics, Oxford
Printed by M & A Thomson Litho Ltd, East Kilbride, Scotland

Oxford University Press, Walton Street, Oxford OX2 6DP

Oxford New York
Athens Auckland Bangkok Bombay
Calcutta Cape Town Dar es Salaam Delhi
Florence Hong Kong Istanbul Karachi
Kuala Lumpur Madras Madrid Melbourne
Mexico City Nairobi Paris Singapore
Taipei Tokyo Toronto
and associated companies in
Berlin Ibadan

Oxford is a trade mark of Oxford University Press

First published 1992
Reprinted 1994

ISBN 0 19 913366 2

CONTENTS

Part 1 EARTH'S UNSTABLE CLIMATE

Part II TIMESCALES OF CLIMATE CHANGE

Part III EXERCISES

Part I
EARTH'S UNSTABLE CLIMATE

'I had a dream, which was not all a dream.
The bright sun was extinguish'd, and the stars
Did wander darkling in the eternal space,
Rayless, and pathless, and the icy earth
Swung blind and blackening in the moonless air;
Morn came and went – and came, and brought no day,
And men forgot their passions in the dread
Of this their desolation; and all hearts
Were chill'd into a selfish prayer for light.'

Byron, July 1816, describing atmospheric conditions during the 'year without a summer' that followed the volcanic eruption of Tambora in 1815.

1 ISSUES AND CONTROVERSIES

In recent years there has been a dramatic change in our awareness of environmental issues. Considered as a whole, the environmental worries of the last few decades have now merged into a single-hearted concern about the future of life on earth. High on the agenda for discussion are future changes in climate. It is now considered to be an issue of considerable political importance. What better for a politician than to be able to talk about global catastrophes and ways in which greenhouse overheating might be prevented, the ozone hole might be closed, or Venice may be saved from inundation by a rising sea-level. Western governments have, only in the last few years, turned *green* in response to widespread concerns about the global environment.

Since the problem of climate change is global in nature, governments have tended to look for global solutions. Millions of pounds have been spent on the development of sophisticated computer simulations of global atmospheric and oceanic circulation, and these have been used to predict future trends. However, we cannot evaluate the present climate, or predict future events, without paying attention to past climate changes. Specifically, it is vital to focus on the following two questions:

1. Have there been periods of climate change during the earth's history that might have been similar in nature to those changes that are presently taking place?
2. What can we learn from these changes that might help us in the prediction of future climate changes?

There are many inter-related issues to be considered. For example, is it possible to measure the *greenhouse effect*? What effect is this having on *global warming*, and what can be done to prevent global *overheating*? Similarly, is it possible to isolate the effect of *ozone layer destruction* on global

◀ *A storm wave batters the coastal defences. An increase in the number and severity of storms could indicate climate change*

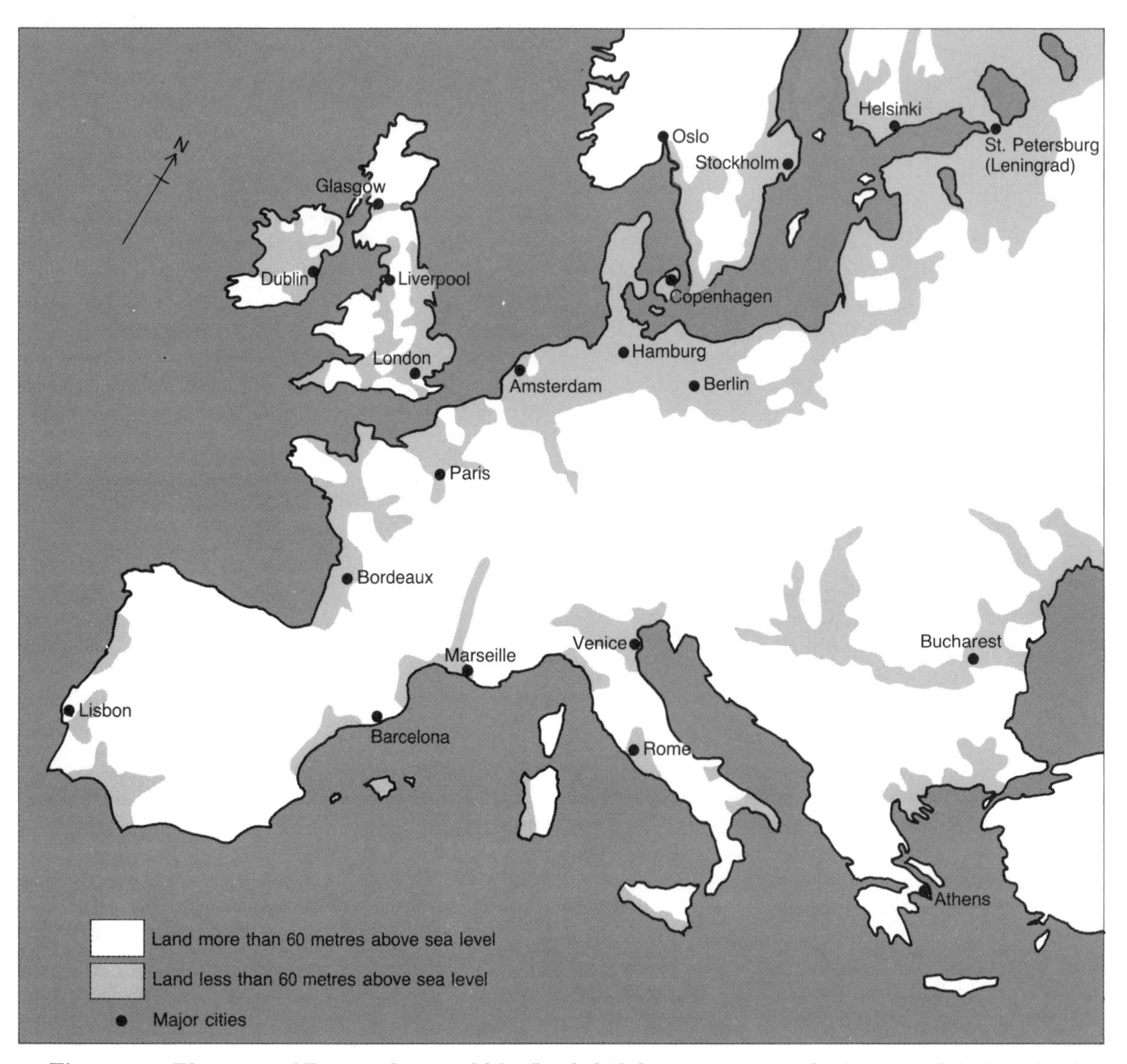

Figure 1.1 *The areas of Europe that would be flooded if there was a rise of +60 m in global sea-level*

climate? What measures can be taken to restore ozone in the atmosphere?

Most computer models suggest that one result of these (and other) environmental changes would be a worldwide rise in sea-level. Figure 1.1 shows how the map of Europe might change. Is it possible to measure the global rise that is presently taking place? What is the likely rate of sea-level rise over the next few decades? Is there anything that can be done to slow down the rate of sea-level rise? What effect will these changes have on future patterns of global atmospheric and oceanic circulation? Where are the future floods and droughts likely to take place? What will happen in the future to the *breadbaskets* of the world and where will famine strike?

This discussion will consider past climate changes that have taken place on the earth. It is based on the premise that the past contains much information of great value in considerations of present trends and future changes in climate. This information can then be used to focus on the important issues concerning the earth's climate today.

First, it is necessary to define what we mean when we talk of *weather* and *climate*.

1.1 Weather and climate

The term *climate* represents the total experience of the *weather* at any place over some specific period of time. Many people refer to climate as *average weather*, but Professor Lamb has argued that this is incorrect since climatic statistics should include reference to *extremes* and *frequencies* of occurrence. This is highlighted by media references to the variability in Britain's present climate. For example, the hot summers and associated drought conditions of 1989 and 1990 have been contrasted with the unsettled summers of the mid-1980s, while the relatively mild winters of the late 1980s have been contrasted with other snowy winters. The great storms of early 1990 were extreme phenomena.

We can begin to understand the principal controversies surrounding our present climate by considering the long-term evolution of the earth's climate. But it is first necessary to consider the vertical structure of the atmosphere and the way that it forms a fragile shield protecting the earth from overheating. It is also essential to consider how the emission of radiation from the sun influences the atmospheric shield.

2 THE ATMOSPHERIC SHIELD

2.1 The troposphere

Viewed in cross-section, the earth's atmosphere consists of a number of layers (Figure 1.2). Most of the atmospheric gases occur in the lower layer, the *troposphere*, which has a thickness of 15–16 km above the equator and as little as 5 or 6 km above the poles. The troposphere is a turbulent layer of the earth's atmosphere with the weather at its base being largely driven by patterns of air flow above. Within the troposphere there is an average decrease in temperature with increasing altitude of about 6.5°C per kilometre. At the top of the troposphere, at the *tropopause*, air temperature may be as low as −50° to −70°C. Belts of high velocity winds known as *jet streams* occur within the upper parts of the troposphere, and these play an important role in the patterns of atmospheric circulation that occur near the earth's surface.

2.2 The stratosphere

Above the tropopause is a layer known as the *stratosphere*. This extends up to approximately 50 km above the earth's surface. In this region of the upper atmosphere, temperatures are relatively constant in the lower parts but they increase at higher levels. This temperature

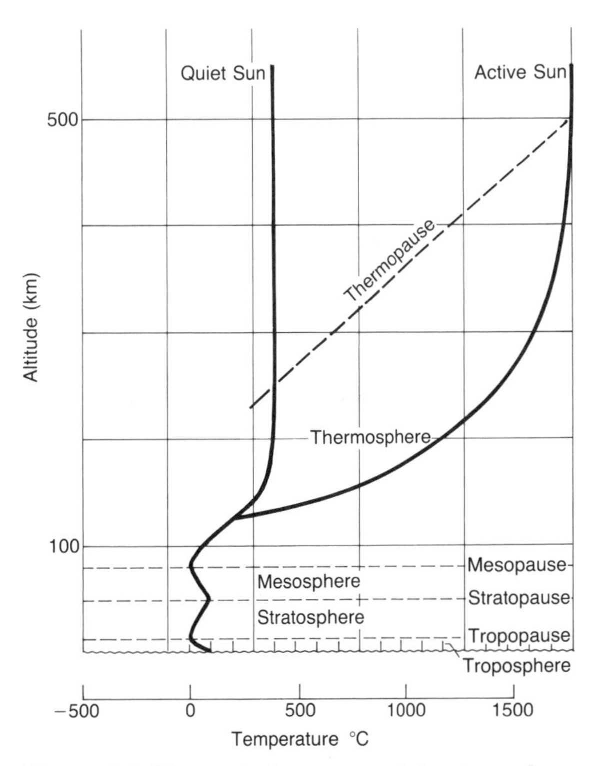

Figure 1.2 The vertical structure of the atmosphere, showing temperature profiles for both a quiet and an active sun

gradient prevents air in this region from becoming turbulent. An unusual characteristic of the stratosphere is that there is a tendency for the winds to change direction every 26 months. This phenomenon is poorly understood, but it may have a very important influence on circulation in the troposphere. The stratosphere also contains most of the *ozone* gas in the atmosphere. Although only very small amounts of this gas are present in this region, its presence is vital for the survival of life on earth since it filters out much of the harmful incoming *ultraviolet* radiation. The stratosphere is also important because it is within this layer that most meteorites are burned out as they enter the earth's gravitational field.

At the top of the stratosphere, temperatures are similar to those occurring at sea-level. The warmth of this region is mostly due to the direct absorption of the sun's ultraviolet rays by ozone. The relatively uniform temperatures tend to inhibit air from moving up and down and because of this the stratosphere acts as a lid that confines air turbulence to the troposphere. Jet aircraft fly in the lower stratosphere and passengers are often able to look down on the ceiling of cloud at the top of the troposphere. The air in the stratosphere is relatively dry since it is largely cut off from the sources of moisture in the troposphere.

2.3 The mesosphere

The upper limit of the stratosphere is known as the *stratopause* (Figure 1.2). Above this boundary is a layer known as the *mesosphere.* In the mesosphere there is a steady decline in the temperature with increasing altitude. This zone mostly occurs between 50 and 85 km altitude. Within the mesosphere the amount of atmospheric gases is very low. The top of the mesosphere is the coldest part of the earth's atmosphere, with temperatures as low as −95°C.

2.4 The thermosphere

Above the mesosphere there is again an increase in temperature. This layer, known as the *thermosphere*, gradually merges with the outer edge of the earth's atmosphere. Within the thermosphere gas concentrations are extremely low, while at altitudes above 500 km some of the gas molecules are able to escape the gravitational pull of the earth. The influence of solar radiation on the gases that are present in the thermosphere and mesosphere results in the creation of many electrically-charged particles known as *ions.* Those ions with the lowest densities (for example, hydrogen and helium) occur at high levels in the thermosphere, while heavier ions settle at lower altitudes. The thermosphere and mesosphere together are known as the *ionosphere.*

2.5 Spatial variations in atmospheric circulation

The reconstruction of past changes in climate would be very easy if periods of increased warmth or cold occurred at approximately the same time throughout the world. Instead, changes in the earth's climate often produce unexpected outcomes. For example, certain areas of the Pacific Ocean were warmer than present during the last Ice Age. In the short term, periods of increased warming over Europe have often been accompanied by severe cooling in Alaska. Similarly, decreased rainfall over the British Isles is often paralleled by increased rainfall over Iceland. These examples illustrate the complex way in which air circulates in the troposphere – something that is central to the issue of global climate change.

i) General circulation patterns

The general circulation of the troposphere conforms to an approximately regular pattern (Figure 1.3). In the tropics, hot air rises and leads to the development of low pressure. Here, the rising air spreads polewards in the upper troposphere and eventually descends in the middle latitudes. The sinking air leads to the

Figure 1.3 *Comparison of patterns of global atmospheric pressure during January and July showing principal areas of high and low pressure as well as prevailing winds*

The arrows fly with the wind: the heavier the arrow, the more regular ('constant') the direction of the wind

Pressure reduced to sea-level

H high pressure cell
L low pressure cell
995–1035 millibars

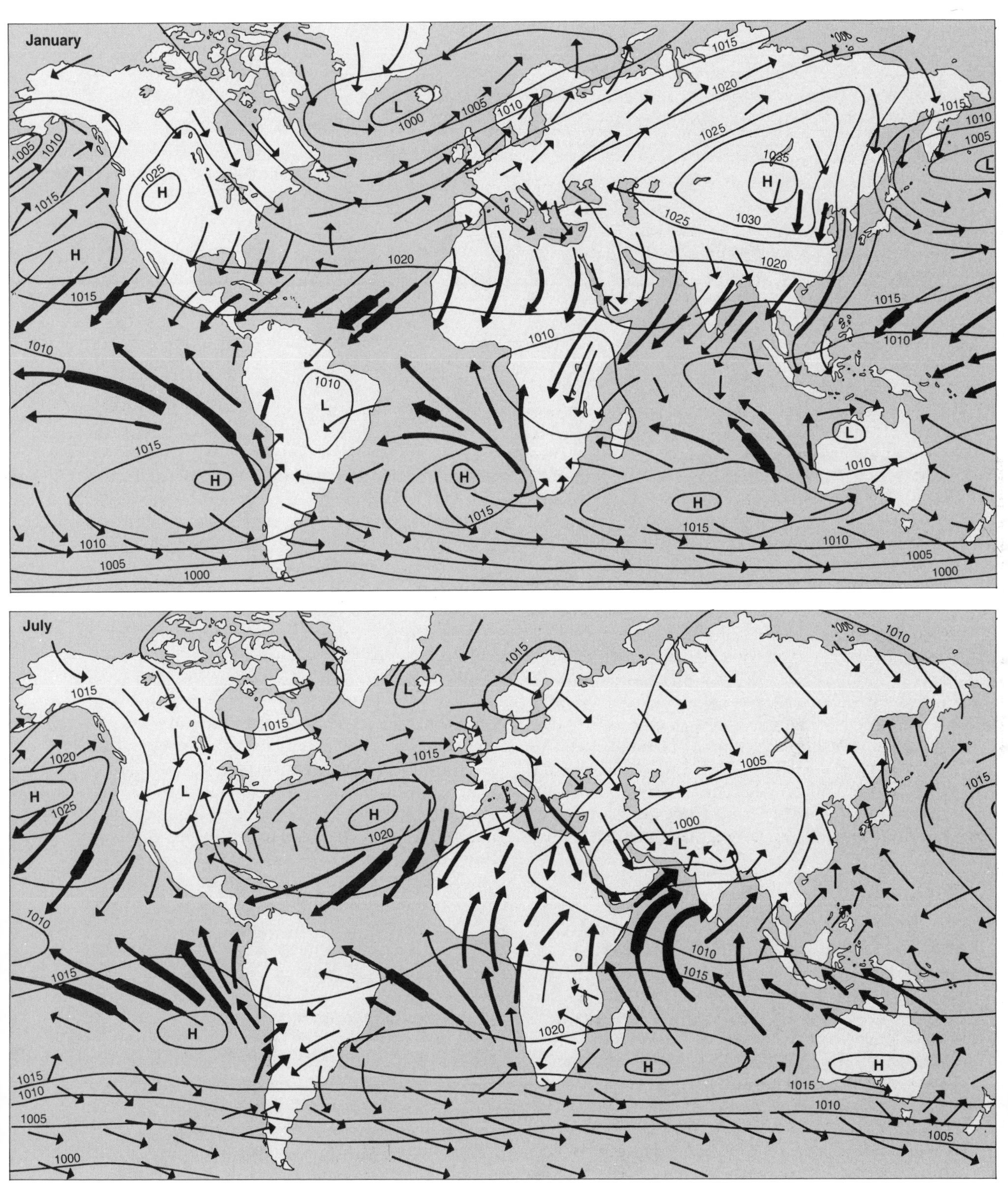
January
1015
1020
1000
1005
1010
1025
1035
1030
H
L
July
1015
1010
1005
1020
1025
1000
H
L

development of several large areas of subtropical high pressure. These cells are permanent features of global atmospheric circulation and occur over oceans and continents. On the equatorial margin of these anticyclones are the *trade winds* that maintain a consistent flow from the north-east in the northern hemisphere and the south-east in the southern hemisphere. The trade winds are constant features of global atmospheric circulation and blow in the opposite direction to the rotation of the earth. By blowing in this manner, the trade winds help to maintain a balance of angular momentum over the earth's surface and act to prevent the earth from spinning faster.

The coldest air masses occur over the poles. Cold air is relatively dense and is therefore relatively stable. Generally, the air tends to sink and is thus characterised by high pressure. This is particularly evident over ice sheets and oceans possessing a cover of sea ice. For example, the Antarctic and Greenland ice sheets are associated with permanent areas of high pressure. Similarly, the sea ice cover over the Arctic Ocean during winter leads to the development of a high pressure air mass over its surface. The cold and relatively dense polar air drifts towards the middle latitudes where it comes into contact with much warmer and less dense air. Since air masses of different densities do not mix easily, the warmer and less dense air is forced to rise above the cold air and only slowly mixes with it. Consequently, the middle latitudes are areas of great air instability, where the rising air masses are associated with the birth, growth, and decay of cyclonic storms.

ii) The influence of the jet stream

The interaction of cold and warm air masses in the middle latitudes is influenced to a large extent by a belt of high velocity winds in the upper troposphere known as the *jet stream*. In the northern hemisphere, these winds occur at an altitude of 8–10 km above sea-level and blow from west to east (Figure 1.4). Above the tropics they flow in a streamlined pattern from east to west. The position of the world's major mountain ranges have an important influence on the pattern of jet stream flow in the middle latitudes of the northern hemisphere. For example, the jet stream over the North Pacific is almost always steered northwards around the Rocky Mountains and thereafter descends southwards across the Great Plains of North America.

Figure 1.4 *Development of upper-air waves in the westerlies showing meandering and streamlined patterns of jet stream flow. 'R' denotes approximate position of Rockies*

The position of the middle latitude jet stream is not fixed. In winter it tends to become displaced southwards. By contrast, it moves northwards during summer and its flow becomes weaker due to the lower temperature contrast between the tropics and the polar regions. The path of jet stream flow across the northern hemisphere also changes from a highly streamlined flow to a meandering and sluggish movement. The precise cause of this change is not known, but it is thought to be closely related to changes in the transfer of angular momentum as the earth rotates. The climatic effects are very clear: meandering and sluggish flow leads to static or blocked air circulation. In summer months, prolonged droughts across Europe are usually associated with blocking anticyclones (for example, the summers of 1976, 1984, and 1989). By contrast, blocking anticyclones during winter are often the cause of severe and prolonged cold conditions. Yet another contrast is the streamlined jet stream flow associated with the great storms that swept across North-West Europe during January and February 1990.

It is clear that patterns of jet stream flow have varied considerably over time. The changes that have taken place in the historical past have often been quite considerable and have exerted a significant influence on climate. The importance of jet stream behaviour on our climate has led to considerable research being undertaken on why it is capable of such sudden changes.

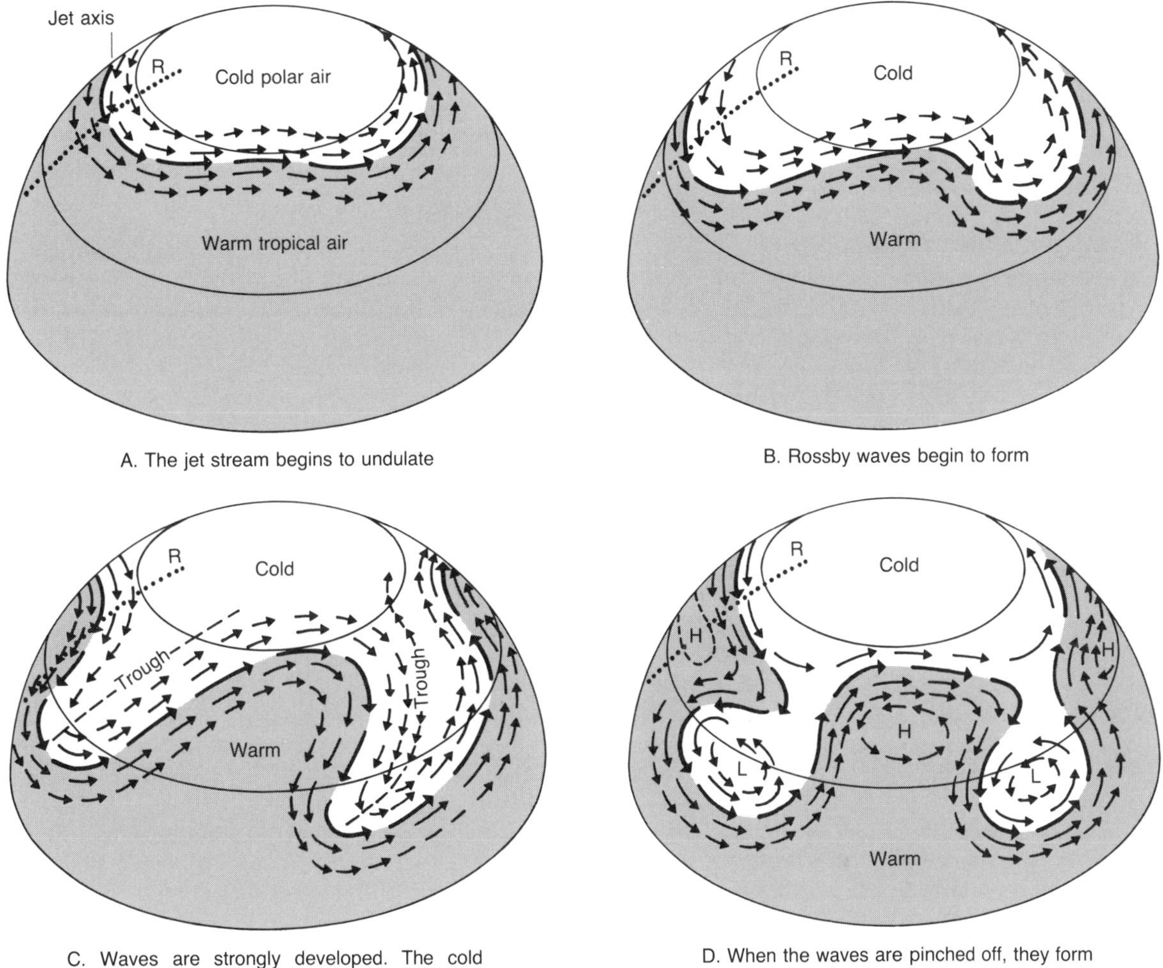

A. The jet stream begins to undulate

B. Rossby waves begin to form

C. Waves are strongly developed. The cold air occupies troughs of low pressure

D. When the waves are pinched off, they form cyclones of cold air

3 FACTORS AFFECTING CLIMATE CHANGE

There are many factors that influence climate change. The most fundamental element is the sun itself. Surprisingly, solar radiation is not constant – it fluctuates in a cyclical manner. On certain occasions, flares occur on the sun's surface and lead to complex changes in the atmosphere. Climate changes are also greatly influenced by the gases in the earth's atmosphere that absorb, scatter, and reflect solar radiation. Some of the gases are crucial to life on earth, and subtle changes in their relative proportions in the atmosphere can lead to drastic changes in climate. The earth's climate may also be altered in a dramatic manner by large volcanic eruptions. These often lead to periods of global climate cooling. Less perceptible, yet also of great importance, are changes in the orbit of the earth around the sun. These appear to have played an important role in shaping the long-term evolution of the earth's climate. Together, these processes operate in a complex manner, the details of which are not yet fully understood.

3.1 Solar radiation

i) Electromagnetic radiation

Life on earth depends on a continuous supply of radiant energy from the sun. In terms of climate change, it is essential to understand the ways in which solar radiation drives the earth's climate system and the ways in which the amount of radiation received by the earth may have changed over time. The amount of incoming solar radiation is highly variable due to changes in the temperature on the sun's surface. These often sudden and violent changes on the surface of the sun have profound effects on the behaviour of the earth's atmosphere.

The very high temperatures on the sun's surface result in the emission of radiation ranging from very short wavelength *gamma* rays to long wavelength *radio* waves (Figure 1.5). Most of the solar radiation that reaches the edge of the earth's atmosphere occurs in the wavelength range between 0.38 and 0.72 microns (a micron is one-millionth of a metre) and corresponds to the visible spectrum. A smaller proportion occurs in the *infrared* range between 0.72 and 1.5 microns. The peak wavelength frequency for incoming solar radiation is approximately 0.5 microns and corresponds to that of blue light (Figure 1.5). When flares occur on the surface of the sun, and temperatures become higher, considerably greater quantities of short-wave radiation are emitted (for example, *gamma, x-ray, and ultraviolet radiation*).

When solar radiation penetrates the earth's atmosphere some is absorbed by the atmosphere and some is reflected back to space, with only about half reaching the earth's surface. In the outer regions of the thermosphere, the relatively small amounts of gases are bombarded by radiation, resulting in the production of electrically-charged particles known as *ions*. In the lower stratosphere and troposphere, the much denser concentration of gases through which solar radiation has to penetrate prevents significant ionisation from taking place. In contrast, in the intermediate sections of atmosphere, the bombardment by solar radiation of relatively large amounts of gases causes the production of large numbers of ions. Many of these are oxygen ions and are of great importance to the earth's climate since they affect the production of ozone.

ii) Solar flaring

The thermo-nuclear reactions that take place near the sun's surface often lead to the occurrence of major solar flares. The increase in surface temperatures, to values well in excess of 7000°C, causes pronounced increases in the amount of emitted short-wave radiation (Figure 1.5). For this reason, the principal effect on the earth of a flaring sun is a marked increase in incoming short-wave radiation rather than a hotter earth. Measurement of the amount of solar energy reaching the outer edge of the earth's atmosphere has shown that solar radiation output fluctuates in a crude cyclical manner. There appear to be numerous cycles of solar activity, but the best-known is an 11-year cycle characterised by a peak phase of flaring and the development of *sunspots* approximately halfway through each cycle (Figure 1.6).

A very strong period of solar flaring commenced on 6th March 1989 and lasted for nearly two weeks. Considerable disturbances took place within the earth's ionosphere and many problems developed in the operation of satellites, telecommunications, and navigation systems. The period of flaring was also associated with the occurrence of exceptionally clear aurora (both the *Aurora Borealis* and the *Aurora Australis*) at low and high latitudes. Brilliant aurora were observed across the USA on the nights of Sunday 12th and Monday 13th March. Similarly intense aurora were observed in northern Australia, Mexico, and Britain. Some scientists believe that the peak of activity will occur during the early 1990s and will subsequently diminish. Certainly, numerous flare events are taking place at the present time. The issue of solar flaring is particularly important since much of the earth's warming that has been attributed to the greenhouse effect might, in part at least, be due to the effects of flaring.

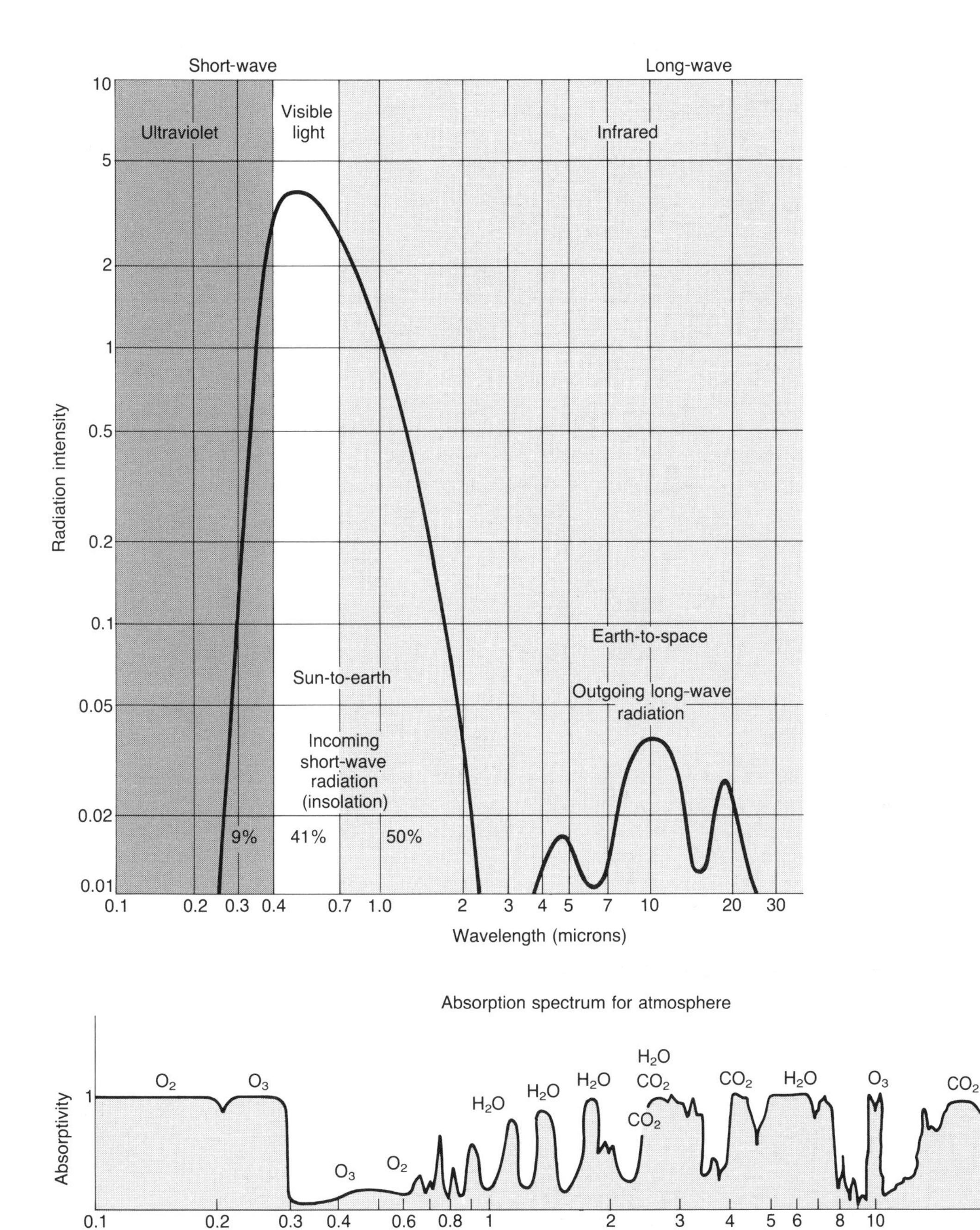

***Figure 1.5** Spectrum of incoming solar electromagnetic radiation and outgoing long-wave radiation (top). Also shown (bottom) is the absorption spectrum for the atmosphere. CO_2 = carbon dioxide, O_2 = oxygen, and O_3 = ozone*

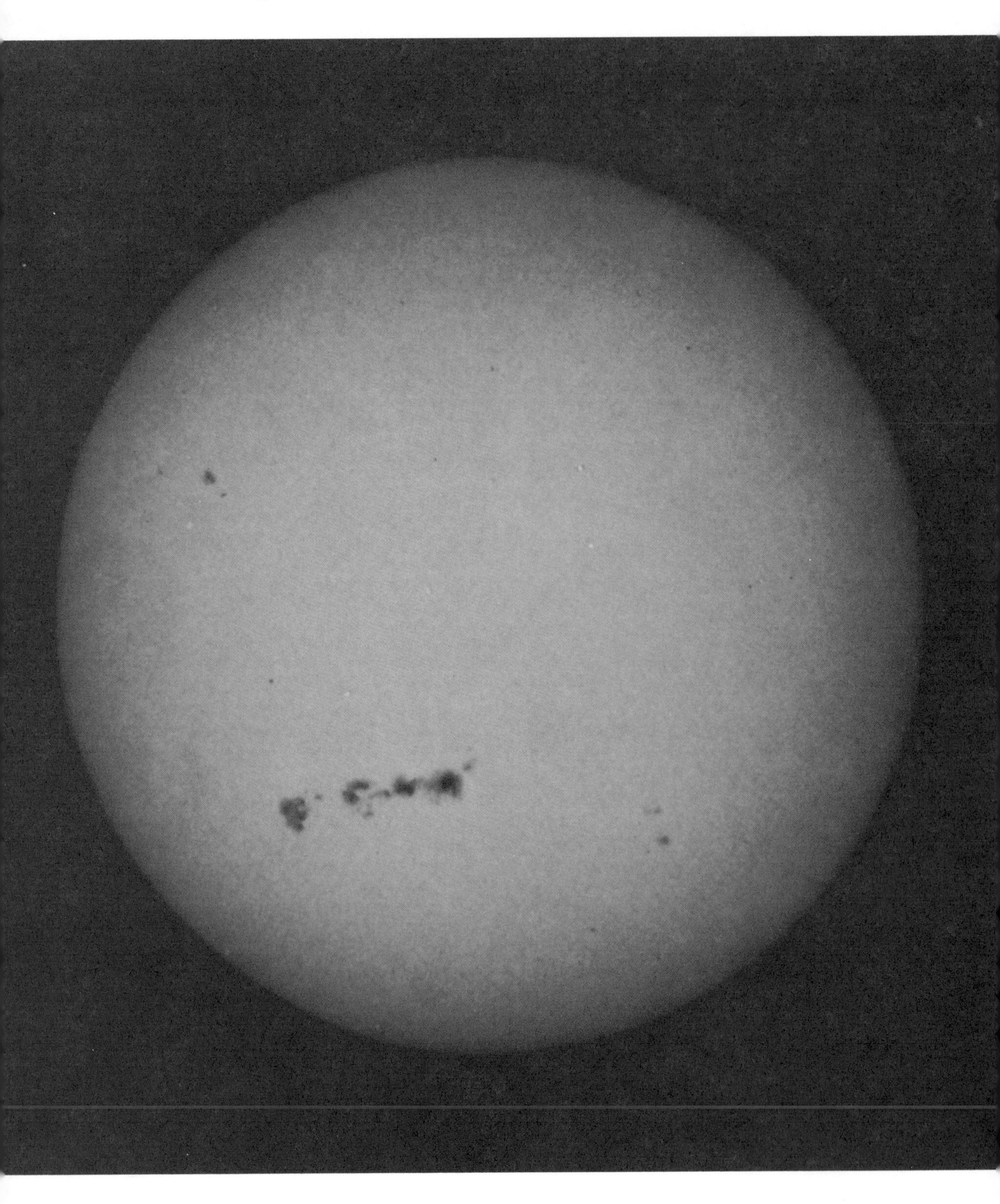

Figure 1.6 *A photograph of the sun, showing a number of large sunspots. This picture was taken a few months before the maximum in the 11-year cycle of solar activity*

3.2 Atmospheric gases: heating and cooling

In general terms, the response of the atmosphere to solar radiation is threefold: absorption, scattering, and reflection. Changes in the concentration of atmospheric gases will induce global changes in temperature.

i) Absorption

Incoming solar radiation is mostly absorbed by ozone, water vapour, carbon dioxide, and dust in the atmosphere, although absorption only takes place within certain wavelength ranges. Most short-wave ultraviolet radiation is used to split oxygen molecules in the stratosphere. The electrically-charged oxygen ions recombine in the stratosphere to produce ozone, which in turn absorbs large amounts of ultraviolet radiation, mostly in the wavelength range between 0.22 and 0.29 microns (Figure 1.5). The ozone then sinks to the base of the stratosphere where it slowly drifts towards the poles. Because oxygen and ozone absorb nearly all of the incoming short-wave radiation, the earth's surface is effectively shielded from ultraviolet light. The minute proportion that reaches the earth's surface leads, under favourable circumstances, to deep sun-tans! Alternatively, excessive amounts may cause skin cancer. Ultraviolet radiation penetrates several feet beneath the surface of the ocean. For this reason, swimming does not protect the body from sunburn.

Water vapour also absorbs considerable amounts of solar radiation, but it does not absorb short-wave radiation or radiation in the visible spectrum. However, it absorbs at longer wavelengths, particularly between 0.8 and 20 microns (Figure 1.5). These wavelengths correspond to radiation emitted from the earth's surface. A significant amount of outgoing long-wave radiation is also absorbed by carbon dioxide. The absorption of long-wave radiation by carbon dioxide, methane, and water vapour has come to be known as the *greenhouse effect* owing to the retention of heat by these gases. This keeps the temperature of the atmosphere much higher than it would otherwise be.

ii) Scattering and reflection

Many of the gas molecules and particles of dust in the atmosphere possess diameters that are within the wavelength range of incoming solar radiation. Much incoming radiation, therefore, is scattered into the surrounding atmosphere. For this reason, scattering of the white light in the atmosphere leads to the development of blue skies. Clouds do not absorb much incoming solar radiation. In general, solar radiation either passes through clouds or is reflected by them, indeed some clouds may reflect up to 80 per cent of incoming solar radiation.

iii) Carbon dioxide, methane, and the greenhouse effect

Scientists fear that the dramatic increase in the concentration of greenhouse gases in the atmosphere is leading to profound changes in the world's climate. It has been argued that some of the climatic extremes of recent years may be partly attributable to enhanced greenhouse warming. For example, the prolonged drought in the American Midwest during 1988 may have been due to greenhouse-induced changes. Scientists at the Climatic Research Unit, East Anglia, have studied recent trends in temperature and rainfall change for the northern hemisphere (Figure 1.7). Their models show complex changes in which warming seems to have led to a 1–2 per cent increase in global rainfall, but a decrease over large areas of the USA, Russia, and the Middle East. Temperature increases also vary over the earth's surface, with the highest increases occurring in polar regions.

The greenhouse effect is caused by the blocking of outgoing radiation by a number of gases in the troposphere (see Figure 1.5). Principal among these are carbon dioxide and methane, both of which absorb, scatter, and reflect this radiation. As a result, temperatures in the troposphere are much higher than they would otherwise be. The increase in the amount of carbon dioxide in the atmosphere is largely due to the burning of coal and oil and the removal of large areas of forest cover. Trees are important in this respect since

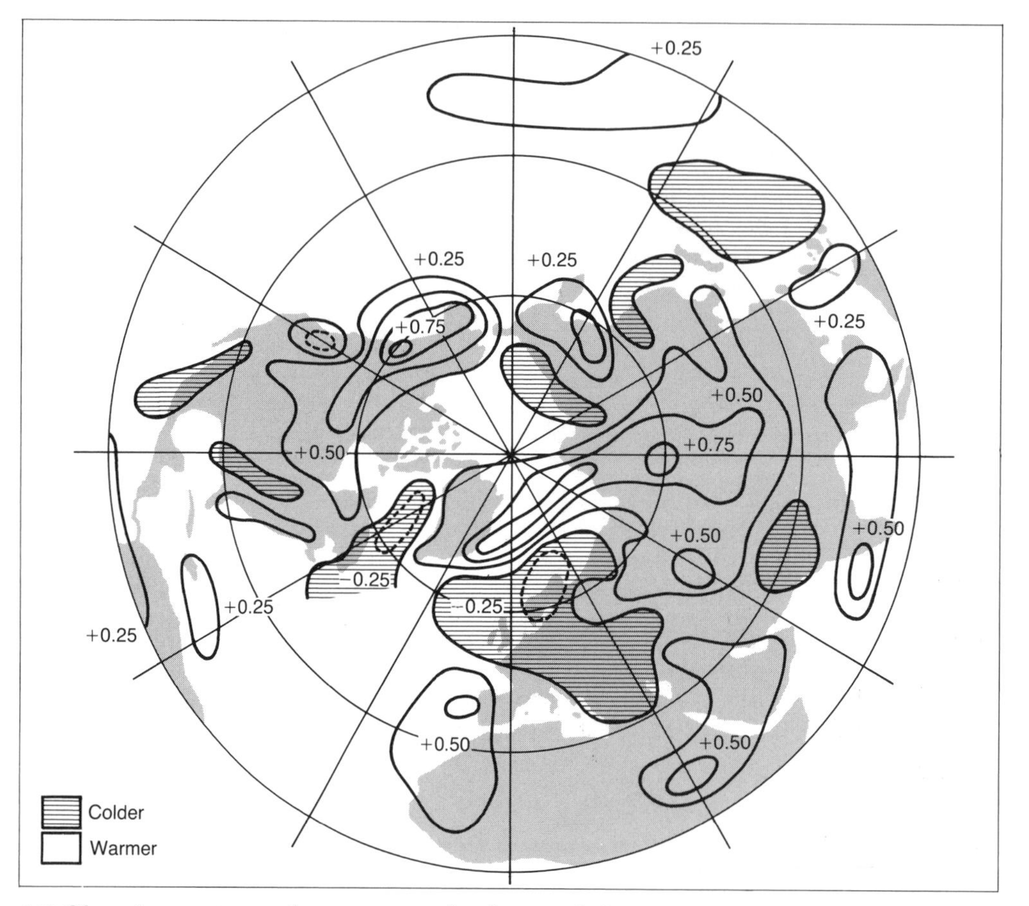

Figure 1.7 Changing patterns of temperature (in degrees Celsius per decade) over the last twenty years (based on the Climatic Research Unit, University of East Anglia)

their growth is dependent upon the absorption of carbon dioxide from the atmosphere. When forest areas are felled, the carbon dioxide is returned to the atmosphere.

Most carbon dioxide, however, is stored in the world's oceans. Not surprisingly, therefore, the total amount of carbon dioxide in the atmosphere is profoundly influenced by the amount and rate of ocean uptake of carbon dioxide from the atmosphere.

Measurement of the atmospheric concentration of carbon dioxide has been undertaken at the Manua Loa Observatory in Hawaii. Since 1957, the concentration has progressively increased from 312 parts per million (ppm) to its present value of 354 ppm (Figure 1.9). The saw-tooth nature of the curve arises because the amount of carbon dioxide in the atmosphere at Manua Loa decreases during the northern hemisphere summer owing to vegetation growth. Conversely, the concentration of carbon dioxide increases again during winter.

Although carbon dioxide is the main greenhouse gas (contributing 50 per cent to the total value), there are additional gases that contribute significantly to the greenhouse effect (Figure 1.9). These include nitrous oxide, chlorofluorocarbons (CFCs), low-level ozone, and methane. Most nitrous oxide accumulates in the atmosphere as a result of the over-use of nitrogen fertilisers on agricultural land. CFCs occur in aerosols as propellants (they constitute the gas that enables the aerosol to be released as a spray) and in refrigerators as coolants. They are also

Figure 1.8 The burning and clearance of the Amazon rainforest could have serious effects on global climate. The Amazon system plays a major role in the way the sun's heat is distributed around the globe; any disturbance could have far-reaching effects. The burning of the rainforest also releases large quantities of carbon dioxide into the atmosphere, adding to the greenhouse effect

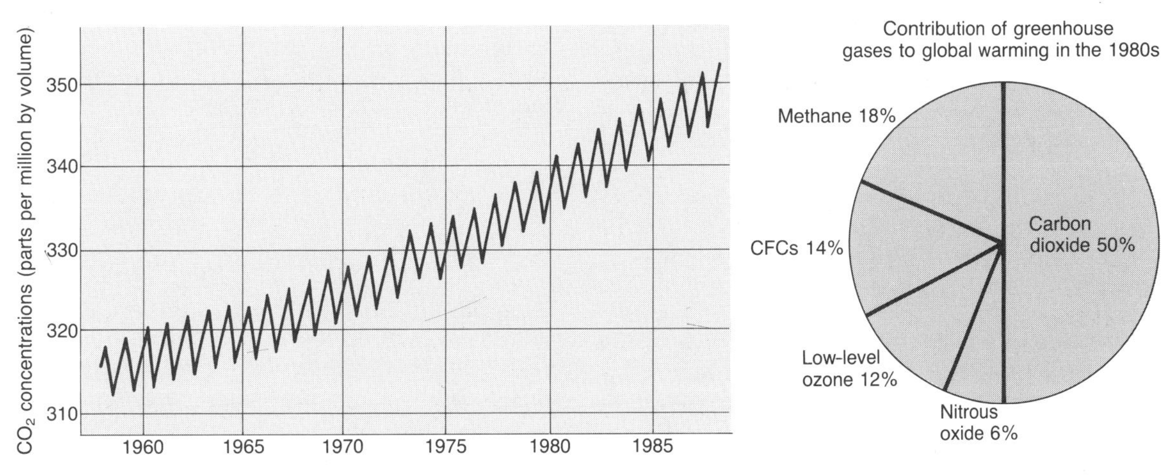

Figure 1.9 The build-up of carbon dioxide in the atmosphere, recorded at Manua Loa Observatory, Hawaii. The contribution of greenhouse gases to global warming during the 1980s is also shown

released into the atmosphere by jet aircraft.

Methane is an important greenhouse gas, contributing about 18 per cent to the total value. It is mostly released into the atmosphere from grazing animals, rubbish tip waste, bogs and marshes, and rice fields. Methane is much more efficient than carbon dioxide in trapping outgoing long-wave radiation and some scientists estimate that within fifty years methane may have become the main greenhouse gas. Methane normally lasts about ten years in the atmosphere before it is lost through its reaction with oxidizing bacteria and other chemical processes. We can study changes in the global amount of methane by looking at ice cores. Methane is trapped in air bubbles in ice cores and measurements of these for the historical period have shown that methane concentrations remained essentially unaltered until about 300 years ago. Since then there has been a progressive increase in atmospheric methane and it is the future projection of this rate of increase that is worrying scientists.

iv) The ozone layer

a) Ozone production

Ozone in the atmosphere is produced when atoms of oxygen (O) collide and combine with molecules of oxygen (O_2) in the presence of *catalytic particles* such as nitrogen. The single atoms of oxygen are created when molecules of oxygen are split by short-wave solar radiation. Most of the ozone in the atmosphere occurs at an altitude of about 25 km. The occurrence of ozone at this particular altitude reflects the balance of two factors: the presence of sufficient short-wave radiation to split oxygen molecules and an adequate density of particles to enable enough collisions to take place.

If all of the ozone in the atmosphere was transferred to sea-level, it would form a layer no more than a few millimetres thick. However, despite the small amounts that occur in the atmosphere, ozone is very important since it absorbs much of the incoming ultraviolet radiation from the sun and thus protects the earth's surface from this harmful radiation.

b) Ozone destruction

Ozone is principally broken down by free *chlorine* atoms to produce chlorine monoxide (ClO) and oxygen. The chlorine monoxide reacts with oxygen to produce more oxygen molecules and a large number of chlorine atoms. As this process of chlorine release continues, large quantities of ozone are removed from the atmosphere. The chlorine that causes the destruction of ozone is released into the atmosphere by the decomposition of CFCs above the ozone layer. At present, approximately 800 000 tonnes of CFCs are produced every year. Most of the chlorine-bearing CFCs are released into the troposphere. They rise and eventually accumulate in the middle and upper stratosphere. In this area, ultraviolet radiation breaks down the molecules and causes the chlorine to sink down into the ozone layer.

This sinking is also favoured by the vertical temperature profile of the stratosphere, where the increase in temperature with increasing altitude promotes the drift of ozone to the polar regions. The chemical reactions that cause the breakdown of ozone require the energy of sunlight. For this reason, large quantities of chlorine accumulate in the ozone layer as an inert gas during the polar winter. Then, during spring, the presence of ultraviolet light leads to ozone breakdown, a reaction that is accelerated by clouds of ice particles in the atmosphere.

c) Ozone holes

The occurrence of an *ozone hole* over Antarctica was first noticed in 1981 and it has increased in size ever since (Figure 1.10). More recently an ozone hole has been detected over the Arctic. Measurements in the Arctic stratosphere have shown that the concentration of chlorine monoxide was at least 50 times higher than predicted and capable of destroying large quantities of Arctic ozone.

The creation of ozone holes over the poles threatens to disturb global climate in several ways. The main problem is the destruction of the shield that protects the earth's surface from damaging ultraviolet radiation. Increased ultraviolet radiation is likely to lead to a greater incidence of skin cancer. It may also have a damaging effect on the ecology of polar oceans since it affects the uptake of carbon dioxide by plankton. Such dramatic changes in the composition of the stratosphere would also lead to major changes in the overall circulation of the

Dark areas show the spread of the Antarctic ozone hole

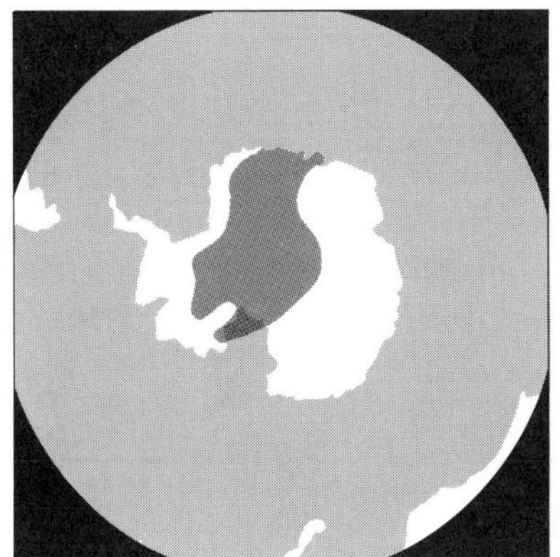
1981

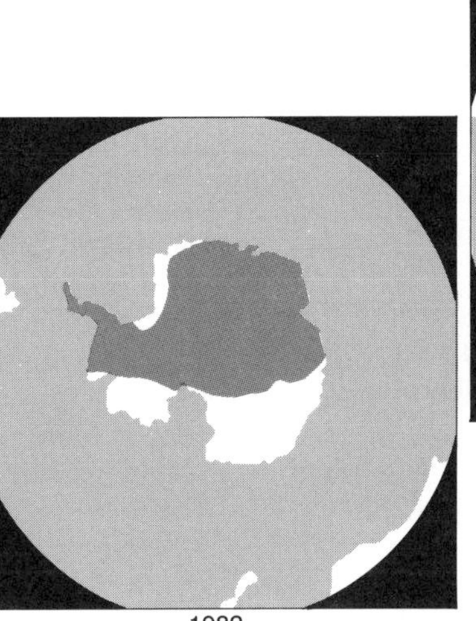
1982

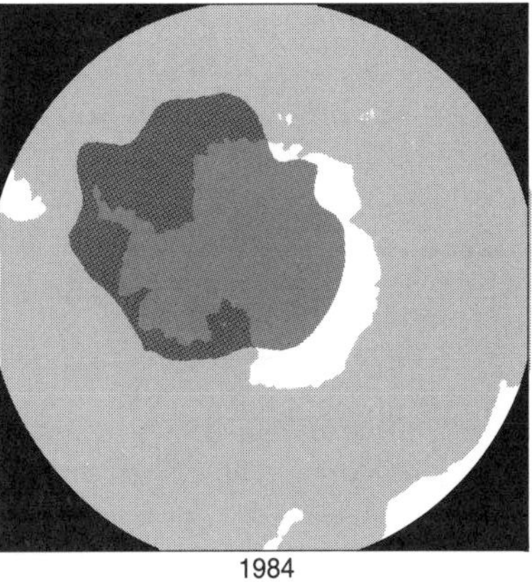
1984

Figure 1.10 *The ozone hole over Antarctica*

atmosphere. An additional effect of an ozone hole over the Antarctic continent would be the accelerated melting of the East and West Antarctic ice sheets. Widespread melting of ice in West Antarctica could lead to a drastic rise (perhaps up to 6 m) in world sea-level.

Joe Farman, the British scientist who first detected the ozone hole over Antarctica, considers that all of the ozone that can be seasonally removed from the Antarctica stratosphere is being removed and that the region is almost completely barren in ozone. Recently, an international agreement, known as the Montreal Protocol, sought to establish some control over the global emission of CFCs. Under this protocol, the emission of CFCs will still increase, but at a slower rate. Present measurements of stratospheric ozone concentrations suggest that the rate of CFC emission is still too high to prevent massive ozone destruction. At present the concentration of atmospheric chlorine is almost twice that needed to halt the widespread ozone depletion that is taking place.

d) Ozone and the earth's magnetic field

Several scientists have suggested that past changes in the earth's magnetic field may have led to the breakdown of ozone in the stratosphere. At present the earth's magnetic field protects the atmosphere from much of the ionising effects of incoming solar radiation. Changes in the magnetic field, however, would lead to a massive increase in the amount of ions produced in the upper atmosphere. It is thought that this would lead to a large increase in the production of nitric oxide (NO) which would, in turn, lead to the rapid breakdown of ozone. Scientists have argued that during times in the geological past when the earth's magnetic field has changed in direction, there have been drastic increases in the amount of ultraviolet radiation reaching the earth's surface (caused by ozone depletion). Some scientists have gone so far as to suggest that dramatic increases in ultraviolet radiation may have been primarily responsible for the *mass extinction* of several prehistoric species (for example, the dinosaurs).

3.3 Causes of the Quaternary Ice Ages

There is much uncertainty about the causes of the Quaternary Ice Ages. Any explanation must first explain why the Quaternary was characterised by a large number of alternations between glacial cold and interglacial warmth. It must also account for the changeover to severe cooling at the start of the Quaternary. Additionally, it has to explain why the second half of the Quaternary was characterised by much *greater* climatic extremes than the first half. One characteristic which is common to all of the Ice Age theories is that they are all *qualitative* and are thus difficult to test scientifically. Broadly, there are three groups of explanations:

1. those due to geological processes;
2. those caused by ocean-atmosphere changes;
3. those due to changes in the orbit of the earth around the sun.

i) Geological mechanisms

One theory is that the build-up of ice was caused by the separation of the Pacific and Atlantic Oceans due to uplift of the mountains of Central America approximately 3 million years ago. The severing of Pacific and Atlantic Ocean waters may have induced marked cooling of the Atlantic Ocean and the eventual growth of ice sheets over the continents of the northern hemisphere.

Another popular view, which is difficult to prove, is that major explosive volcanic eruptions may have caused the ice ages. Over geological time, sea-floor spreading and continental drift may have resulted in changes in the distribution and shape of continents and ocean basins and, in turn, may have substantially altered global climate. Although this may be true for earlier geological periods, it cannot explain Quaternary climate changes since only small amounts of continental drift have taken place during this period. However, in areas of plate collision, considerable land uplift during the Quaternary may have been sufficient to induce climate change. For example, the Tibetan Plateau may have risen by as much as 3000 m during the last 100000 years, perhaps causing substantial changes in air flow in the troposphere.

A more sensational theory is that a great meteorite impact in the South-East Pacific Ocean induced widespread global cooling during the start of the Quaternary.

ii) Ocean-atmosphere mechanisms

Numerous theories of climate change involve types of feedback between the ocean and the atmosphere. One model is based on the premise that periods of glaciation in the northern hemisphere are associated with the development of vast areas of sea ice over the surrounding oceans (i.e. the Arctic Ocean and the North Atlantic Ocean). The sea ice cover prevents the evaporation of moisture from the ocean surface and therefore leads to the establishment of dry, cold, and subsiding air. This process, together with the development of large ice sheets over North America, Europe, and Russia, leads, during ice ages, to the creation of almost desert conditions in the middle and high latitudes of the northern hemisphere with nearly all areas dominated by high pressure. In this manner, vast areas of the ice sheets are starved of precipitation and undergo thinning and retreat.

iii) Earth orbital mechanisms

A popular explanation for the onset of ice ages is that they are due to changes in the orbit of the earth around the sun and to changes in the tilt of the earth's axis. These long-term processes appear to have caused important changes in the distribution of solar radiation reaching the top of the atmosphere. They also caused important seasonal differences in the amount of heat received. These processes were first described by *James Croll* in the late nineteenth century and later by *Milutin Milankovitch* in the early twentieth century. They provide an explanation for climate change in which solar radiation is assumed to remain constant over time (Figure 1.11).

Croll and Milankovitch observed that three processes dominate the patterns of earth orbit around the sun (Figure 1.11). The first is that the earth tends to wobble on its axis as it spins. This change, known as the *precession of the equinoxes*, takes place over a 23000-year cycle and causes seasonal variations in the time when the earth is closest to and farthest from the sun. At present, the earth is closest to the sun during the winter solstice and farthest away from it at the summer solstice. However, 11500 years ago, the earth was

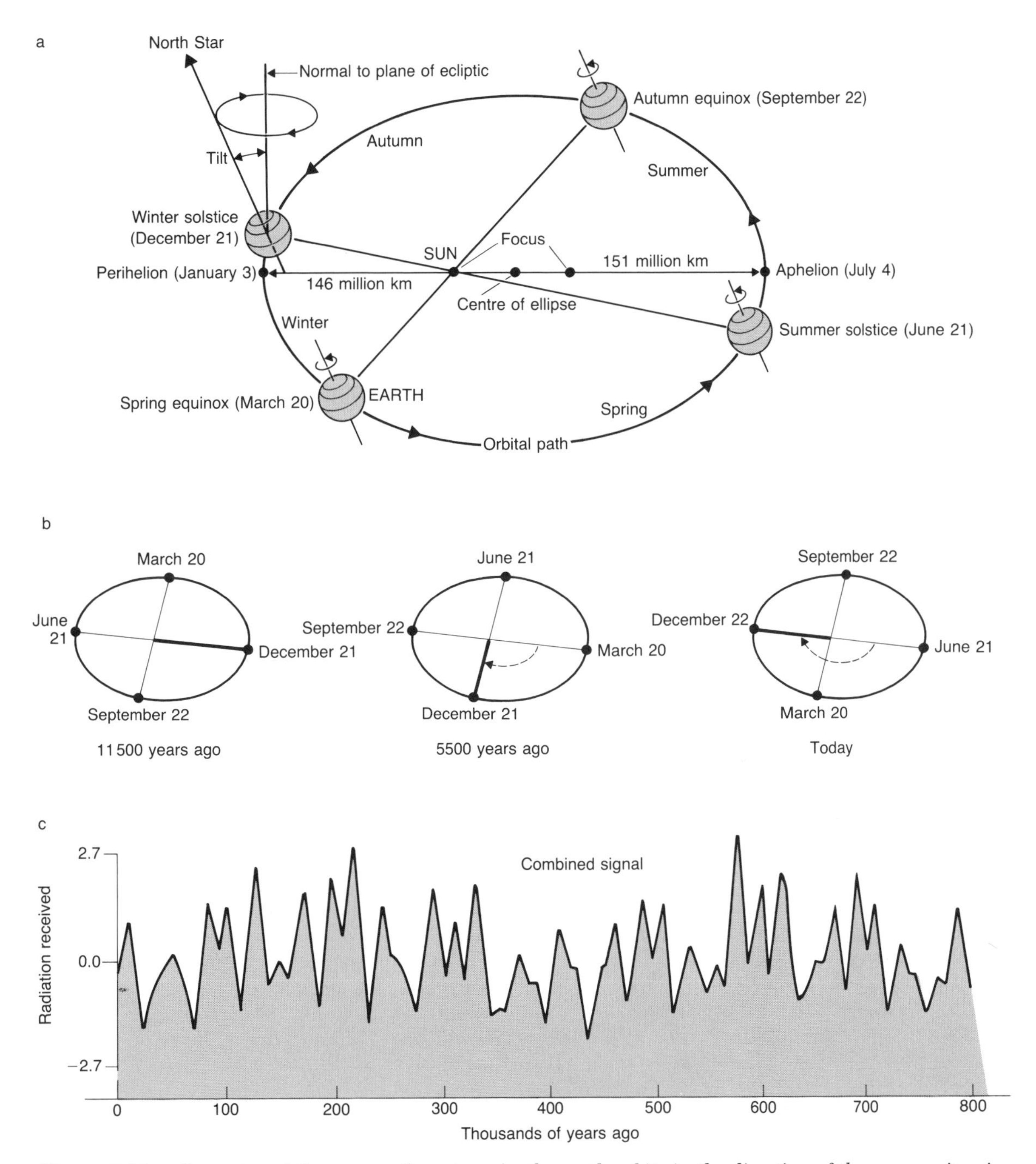

Figure 1.11 **a** *Geometry of the sun-earth system. As the earth orbits in the direction of the arrows, it spins about its own axis which is tilted at 23.5° and points towards the North Star.* **b** *The precession of the equinoxes causes the position of the equinoxes and solstices to slowly shift around the earth's orbit.* **c** *The patterns of orbit eccentricity, axial tilt, and precession for the last 800 000 years. When these factors are combined, they produce an irregular curve (combined signal) that shows changes in the amount of radiation that reaches the earth*

farthest from the sun at midwinter and closest to it in midsummer. There was a greatly exaggerated seasonality in global climate at this time, with colder-than-average winters and warmer-than-average summers.

The second orbital factor is the *tilt of the earth's axis*, presently 23.5°, but varying between approximately 21.39° and 24.36° every 41000 years. During periods when the tilt is very high, the greater extremes of seasonal temperature lead to colder winters and warmer summers.

The third factor is the changing *shape of the earth's orbit* around the sun. This changes from a circular orbit to an eccentric (highly elliptical) orbit and back again over a 96000-year cycle. Again, this cyclical variation leads to changes in the lengths of the seasons, with the greatest contrasts occurring when the orbit is highly eccentric.

iv) Volcanism

a) Global cooling

Scientists have long known that major explosive volcanic eruptions, which produce large quantities of ash, often result in global cooling. Such eruptions are often associated with the injection of large quantities of volcanic ash into the stratosphere where it can persist for several years (Figure 1.12). Dust injected into the troposphere is soon washed out by rain. The ash which occurs in the stratosphere, however, absorbs incoming solar radiation and is heated.

It is generally believed that large low latitude eruptions are likely to cause climate cooling on a global scale whilst those at higher latitudes tend to cause cooling within one particular hemisphere. Professor Lamb attempted to compare the possible climatic effects of the veils of ash caused by different historical eruptions. His *Dust Veil Index (DVI)* has a reference value of 1000, based on the violent eruption in 1883 of Krakatoa in Indonesia (Table 1.1). The table shows a list of the major volcanic eruptions that took place between 1680 and 1970. The DVI attributed by Lamb to each eruption is also given.

b) Giant eruptions

Any detailed study of the nature of volcanic activity over the last 100000 years inevitably reveals a series of remarkable volcanic eruptions. Some of these have undoubtedly influenced global climate. The largest eruption took place 75000 years ago at Toba in northern Sumatra. Volcanic ash was deposited over the Indian Ocean for a distance of 2500 km. The column of ash is believed to have passed vertically through the stratosphere and into the mesosphere, to almost 55 km above the earth's surface. It is thought to have created a dust veil in the atmosphere that would have prevented considerable quantities of radiation from reaching the earth, thus causing global cooling. Some believe that this most gigantic of all Quaternary eruptions contributed to the triggering of an ice age.

A large number of explosive eruptions took place at the end of the last ice age. This could have been because melting ice sheets led to rapid uplift of land surfaces. Under such unstable conditions, the release of pressure on the earth's crust was accompanied by numerous violent eruptions. The largest of these took place at Glacier Peak in the northern Cascade Range in western USA, while additional eruptions took place in the Eifel Mountains of western Germany and at the Mount Hekla and Katla volcanoes in southern Iceland. One of the Icelandic eruptions, 10600 years ago, spread volcanic ash across most of the North Atlantic Ocean.

c) More recent eruptions

It has been argued by some scientists that the climatic fluctuations that characterised the Little Ice Age (approximately between 1300 and 1900 AD) were intimately related to the unusually high frequency of volcanic eruptions that took place during this period. Professor Lamb has suggested that many of the episodes of cooling which took place over this period were related to the injection of large quantities of volcanic dust into the atmosphere. For example, the dramatic volcanic eruptions at Laki in Iceland during May and June 1783 took place in a decade when several winters were characterised by average temperatures more than 2°C lower than present.

In addition to Laki, several other major volcanic eruptions are known to have been followed by a lowering of global temperatures. For example, as long ago as 1500 BC, the eruption of Santorini in the Aegean Sea (DVI 2500) was followed by a pronounced climate cooling. Perhaps most famous of all is the great eruption

Table 1.1 Major volcanic eruptions during the last 300 years. The associated Dust Veil Index value according to Lamb is also shown for each eruption

Year	*Volcano*	*DVI*
1680	Krakatoa, Indonesia	400
1680	Tongkoko, Celebes	1000
1693	Hekla, Iceland	100
1693	Serua, Molucca Is.	500
1694	Amboina, Molucca Is.	$\nless 250$
1694	'Celebes'	$\nless 250$
1694	Gunung Api, Molucca Is.	400

NOTE: If the low temperatures prevailing in England, as well as Iceland and a wide surrounding region, over the years 1694–8 were representative of a worldwide anomaly of about the same amount, and provided their departure from the temperatures prevailing in the immediately preceding and following years were entirely due to volcanic dust, the total DVI for 1694–8 should be 3000–3500.

Year	*Volcano*	*DVI*
1707	Vesuvius, Italy	150
1707	Santorini	250
1707	Fujiyama, Japan	350
1712	Miyakeyama, Japan	200
1717	Vesuvius, Italy	100
1717	Kirishima Yama, Japan	200
1721	Katla, Iceland	250
1730	Roung, Java	300
1744	Cotopaxi, Ecuador	300
1752	Little Sunda Is., possibly Tambora	1000
1754	Taal, Luzon, Philippines	300
1755	Katla, Iceland	400
1759	Jorullo, Mexico	300
1760	Makjan, Moluccas	250
1763	'Molucca Is.'	600(?)
1766	Hekla, Iceland	200
1766	Mayon, Luzon, Philippines	2300(?)
1768	Cotopaxi, Ecuador	900
1772	Gunung Papandayan, Java	250
1775	Pacaya, Guatemala	1000(?)
1779	Sakurashima, Japan	450
1783	Eldeyjar, off Iceland	
	Laki and Skaptar Jökull, Iceland	700
1783	Asama, Japan	300
	Total veil, 1783:	1000
1786	Pavlov, Alaska	150
1795	Pogrumnoy, Umanak Is., Aleutians	300
1796	Bogoslov, Aleutians	100
1799	Fuego, Guatemala	600
1803	Cotopaxi, Ecuador	1100(?)
1807	Various, including	
–10	Gunung Merapi, Java	(?)
	and São Jorge, Azores	(?)
	Total veil, 1807–10:	1500(?)
1811	Sabrina, Azores	200
1812	Soufrière, St Vincent	300
1812	Awu, Great Sangihe, Celebes	300
1813	Vesuvius, Italy	100
1814	Mayon, Luzon, Philippines	300
1815	Tambora, Sumbawa, Indonesia	3000
1821	Eyjafjallajökull, Iceland	100
1822	Galunggung, Java	500
1826	Kelud, Java	300
1831	Giulia or Graham's Island	200
1831	Pichincha, Ecuador	(?)
1831	Babuyan, Philippines	300
1831	Barbados	(?)
1835	Coseguina, Nicaragua	4000
1845	Hekla, Iceland	250
1846	Armagora, South Pacific	1000
1852	Gunung Api, Banda, Moluccas	200
1856	Cotopaxi, Ecuador	700
1861	Makjan, Moluccas	800
1875	Askja, Iceland	300
1878	Ghaie, New Ireland, Bismarck Archipelago	possibly 1250
1883	Krakatoa, Indonesia	1000
1888	Bandai San, Japan	250
1888	Ritter Is., Bismarck Archipelago	250
1902	Mont Pelée, Martinique	100
1902	Soufrière, St Vincent	300
1902	Santa Maria, Guatemala	600
	Total veil, 1902:	about 1000
1907	Shtyubelya Sopka Ksudatch, Kamchatka	150
1912	Katmal, Alaska	150
1963	Mt Agung (Gunung Agung), Bali	800
1966	Awu, Great Sangihe, Celebes	150–200
1968	Fernandina, Galapagos	50–100
1970	Deception Is.	(200)

of Tambora in Indonesia in April 1815 (Figure 1.13). This eruption was followed in Europe by *the year without a summer*, an event which prompted Byron to write his famous poem 'Darkness'. In this year, temperatures at Madras in India unusually passed below freezing on several occasions. The optical effects of the volcanic dust in the atmosphere led Turner to include red sunsets

Figure 1.12 *A volcanic eruption shoots a column of ash, pulverised rock, and gas into the atmosphere*

Extract from *The Times* 21 November 1815

Extract from a letter, dated the 29th of May, 1815, at Batavia, from a merchant of that place:

"We have had one of the most tremendous eruptions of the mountain Tomboro, that ever perhaps took place in any part of the world; this mountain is situated on the island of Sumbawa, and is distant from Batavia not less than 550 miles. We heard the explosion here distinctly, and had some of the ashes. It was totally dark at Macassar long after the sun was up; and at noon, at Sourabaya, the sun succeeded in enlightening the good folks so far as to allow them to see some yards around; the ashes lay at Macassar which is 250 miles from Sumbawa, 1½ inches deep. Captain Fenn, of the Dispatch, and Captain Eatwell, of the Benares, who have visited the island since the eruption, both declare, that the anchorage is much changed, and that they found the sea for many miles around the island so completely covered with trunks of trees, pumice stone, etc, as to impede materially the progress of the two ships. Captain Eatwell says, he was told, that a village was inundated, and had three fathoms water over it. Great numbers of the miserable inhabitants have perished, and others die daily. The crops of Paddy (Rice) have been utterly destroyed over a great part of the island, so that the situation of the unfortunate survivors will be really pitiable."

Figure 1.13 *An extract describing the eruption of Tambora in April 1815*

in many of his paintings. More recently, in 1982, the eruption of El Chichon in Central America was followed by a marked global cooling. Some scientists have argued that the bad European winters of 1984 and 1985 may have resulted from the effects of this eruption. The likely effects on climate of the June 1991 eruptions of Mt. Pinatubo in the Philippines are not yet known although the eruption is thought to have been the largest this century.

4 ENVIRONMENTAL IMPACTS OF CLIMATE CHANGE

A popular view among scientists is that global warming, caused by the greenhouse effect, is likely to continue into the twenty-first century and beyond. A less popular view, yet one that was widespread in the 1970s, is that another ice age is likely to take place in the near future. Whatever pattern of global climate change lies ahead, there will be important consequences for humankind. One future world will be one characterised by overcooling, the other by overheating.

4.1 Overcooling

There has always been disagreement about the way in which a future ice age would begin. One view is that if the winter snowfall across continental areas persisted into the following spring and summer, this would trigger an *instantaneous* glaciation. Another view is that gradual climate cooling would encourage the growth and advance of valley glaciers in highland areas. This model for the beginning of an ice age is similar to the environmental changes that accompanied the development of the Little Ice Age in Europe during the seventeenth and eighteenth centuries. A more extreme version of the effects of climate cooling is provided by the environmental changes that accompanied the development of the Younger Dryas glaciation between 11 000 and 10 000 years ago (see Part II). Whatever pattern of climate cooling might take place in the future, the impact on humankind would be severe. If the Little Ice Age is taken as a model, there would be a major displacement of the world's climatic zones and a consequent reorganisation of agricultural practices. In Britain, the growing season would be substantially reduced and there would be an increase in storminess and flooding. We might also expect numerous wet and cool summers and prolonged periods of severe winter cold.

4.2 Overheating

Support for overcooling theories has diminished recently due to increased awareness of the influence on global climate of the greenhouse effect and the thinning of the ozone layer. These changes have been accompanied by quantitative studies which have demonstrated that global temperatures have increased slightly during recent decades. In short, the earth seems to be overheating. Scientists at the University of East Anglia have shown that although there has been an overall increase in temperature, there have been significant regional variations with some areas suffering a temperature decrease. Significant changes in the pattern of precipitation have also taken place. These changes in climate are already having a severe impact. For example, it has been suggested that the storms and floods that struck North-West Europe during the winter of 1989–90 were partly a product of greenhouse warming. It is claimed that warmer oceans result in greater evaporation and that the greater amounts of moisture contained within cyclones are leading to more energetic storms and more severe rainfall. The human consequences of global warming are all too obvious. Increased solar radiation, coupled with a thinner ozone layer, implies a greater risk of skin cancer. Much has also been written on the likely effects of greenhouse warming on global ecology. The greatest tragedy of global overheating, however, is sea-level rise.

i) The tragedy of sea-level rise

It is now generally agreed that sea-level is rising at an alarming rate, perhaps as much as 2.5 mm per year. It is self-evident that if this rate of sea-level rise were to continue uninterrupted for several decades many cities would be inundated by the rising waters. The tragedy of coastal flooding would be felt worldwide.

Figure 1.14 *Venice under water. Venice is just one of many places threatened by sea-level rise*

At present, the fastest rates of sea-level rise appear to be taking place in areas where the land is also subsiding. For example, certain areas of Venice are presently flooded 35 times each year. Predictions for future rates of sea-level rise are the subject of disagreement. The most extreme view is that global sea-level will rise by +5 m by 2050 AD. This view is based on the argument that a water temperature rise in the Antarctic Circumpolar Ocean would be sufficient to lead to the disintegration of the West Antarctic ice sheet. A more prudent estimate by the Department of

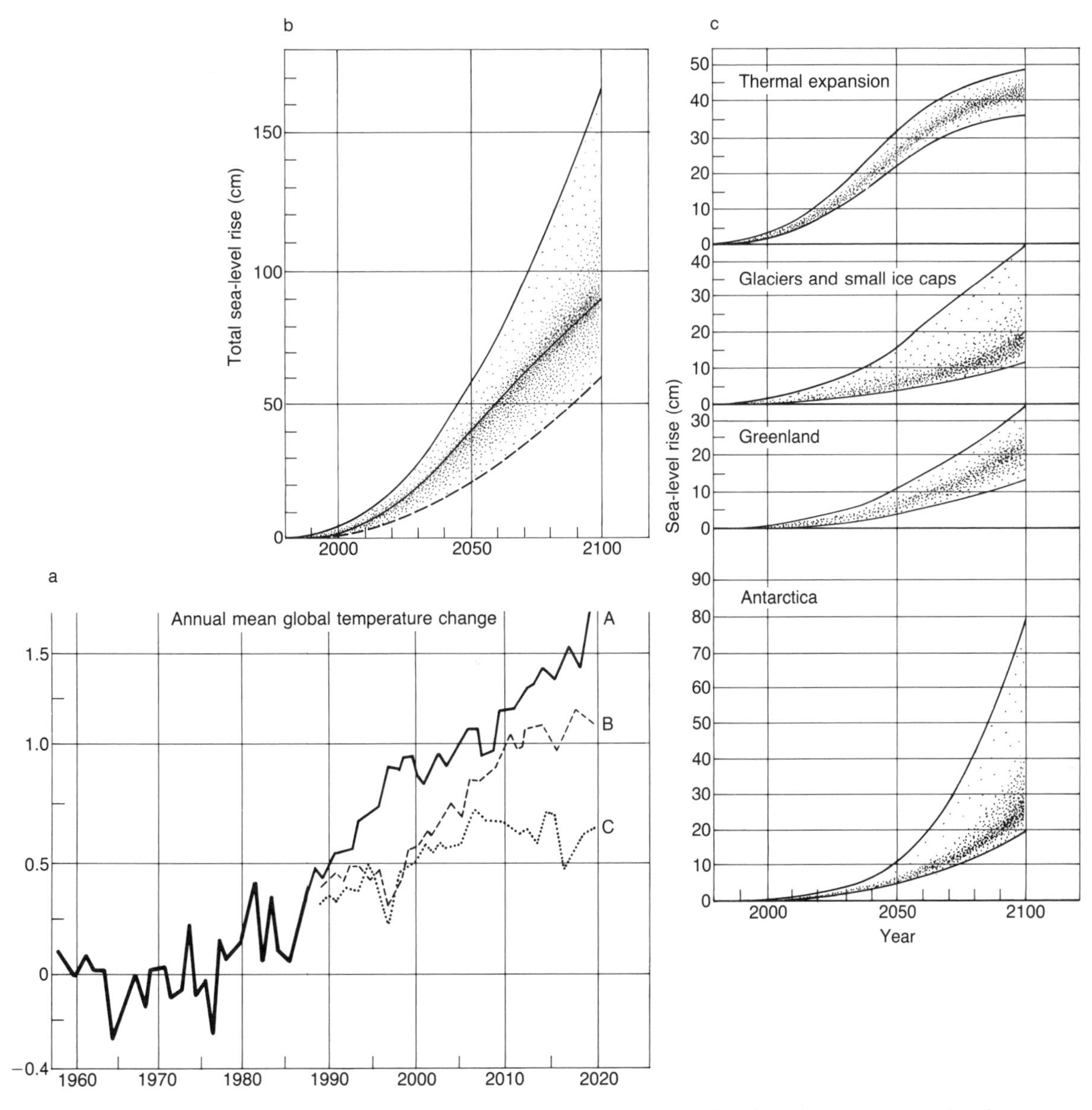

Figure 1.15 **a** *Trends in global temperature during the last 30 years. Predicted temperatures for the next 30 years are also shown.* **b** *Predicted changes in global sea-level to 2100 AD, relative to present with likely upper and lower estimates.* **c** *Proportion of predicted sea-level rise that can be ascribed to different sources*

the Environment, based on modelling of greenhouse warming, is that world sea-level will, on average, rise between 20 and 30 cm by 2030 AD (Figure 1.15). The problem of predicting future sea-level rise is complicated even further by the fact that ocean water expands as air temperatures increase. For example, it is believed that an average air temperature increase of 4.5°C would induce a temperature expansion of the oceans causing a sea-level rise of as much as 30 cm.

Many are of the opinion that a doubling of the carbon dioxide content of the atmosphere will increase the average temperature at the earth's surface by between 1.5 and 4.5°C. Such dramatic increases would cause increased melting of the ice sheets in the polar regions. This, in turn, would lead to a rapid rise in global sea-level. However, *relative sea-level* in some areas would fall. This would be most pronounced around Greenland and Antarctica where the uplift of the land due to decreased ice load would be greater than the rise in sea-level.

5 FINDING EVIDENCE FOR CLIMATE CHANGE

5.1 Long timescales

There are many types of evidence that can be used to reconstruct past changes in climate (Table 1.2). At timescales of between one thousand and one million years, the faunal and floral characteristics of ancient sediments can provide valuable information about past climatic conditions. Former environmental conditions can be accurately deduced on land by geomorphological studies, while detailed stratigraphic information can be obtained by investigating sediment cores taken from the floors of oceans and lakes.

i) Sediment cores

a) Emiliani's discovery

One of the greatest revolutions in our understanding of long-term climate change was based

Table 1.2 Orders of climatic variation

Timescale unit			*Principal bases of evidence*	
(1) Minor fluctuations within the instrumental record	10 years	Minor fluctuations which give the impression of operating over intervals of the order of 25–100 years, with somewhat irregular length and amplitude	(1)	Instrumental; behaviour of glaciers; records of river-flow and lake levels; non-instrumental diaries: crop yields, tree-rings (also for dating).
(2) Post-glacial and historic	10^2 years	Variations over intervals of the order of 250–1000 years, e.g. the sub-Atlantic recession and others affecting vegetation in Europe and North America	(2)	Earlier records of extremes: fossil tree-rings; archaeological finds; lake levels; varves and lake sediments; oceanic core-samples; pollen analysis; radio-carbon dating; ice cores.
(3) Glacial	10^4 years	The phases within an ice age, e.g. the duration of the last Ice Age was of the order of 12×10^4 years	(3)	Fauna and flora characteristic of interglacial deposits; pollen analysis; variation in height of snowline and extent of frozen ground; oceanic core-samples.
(4) Major geological	10^6 years	Duration of ice ages as a whole, periods of evolution of species	(4)	Geological evidence: character of deposits; fossil fauna and flora; dating largely through radio-activity of rocks.

on the discovery that it was possible to measure indirectly past climates through the study of sediments on the floors of the world's oceans. During the 1940s, scientists noticed that cores of mud taken from the ocean floor contained the remains of numerous small animals, known as *foraminifera*, that had previously lived near the ocean surface. *Caesar Emiliani* measured the amounts of heavy *isotopes* of oxygen contained within individual fossils. He made measurements on fossils at different levels in the cores and noticed the proportion of heavy oxygen showed significant changes with depth. Emiliani realised the changing amounts of heavy oxygen in the fossils might provide a record of past climate changes (Figure 1.16).

Emiliani believed fossils which contained a high proportion of heavy oxygen were likely to have lived and died in cool water. By contrast, low values for the oxygen isotopes indicated warmer water temperatures. Emiliani suggested that the oceans may have been subject to seven major cycles of cooling and warming – in other words, there may have been seven ice ages. This was an astonishing assertion since many believed that only four glaciations had taken place in the northern hemisphere (Figure 1.16).

b) Recent developments

More recently, substantial changes have been made to Emiliani's interpretation. The most important change, proposed by *Dansgaard* in Copenhagen and *Shackleton* in Cambridge, is that Emiliani's record is not of water temperature changes but a measure of changes in the volume of water stored in the ocean over time. It is therefore a measure of the *changes in the volume of ice* locked up as ice sheets and glaciers over time.

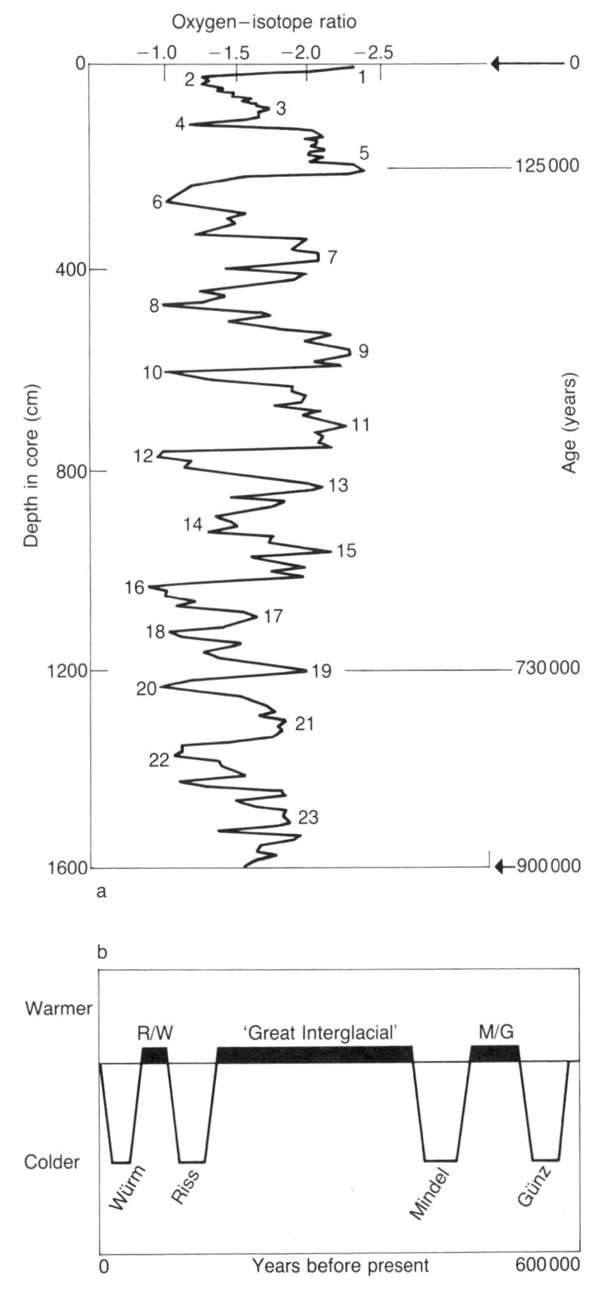

Figure 1.16 **a** *The oxygen isotope curve for the equatorial Pacific showing changes in global ice volume during the last 900 000 years. Note that each glacial/interglacial cycle is about 100 000 years in length. Each warm interval is indicated by an odd number while the cold intervals are indicated by even numbers. Isotope Stage 2, for example, represents the last glacial maximum that culminated at approximately 18 000 years ago.* **b** *The old classical model of Quaternary glaciations, showing four main glacial periods. Note the extent of the 'Great Interglacial'*

To date, hundreds of sediment cores have been sampled from the floors of the world's oceans. The oxygen isotope signals that they portray are all very similar and provide convincing confirmation of global ice volume and sea-level changes. Several sediment core sequences have been recovered which extend the oxygen isotope curve to include several tens of millions of years.

The curves of changing volumes of global ice show that wild fluctuations took place during the last 50 million years. The most dramatic changes occurred during the Quaternary. Twenty or more periods of worldwide glaciation are thought to have taken place during this period, each separated by a period of interglacial warmth. The sawtooth nature of the oxygen isotope curve suggests that many of these changes in climate took place incredibly quickly.

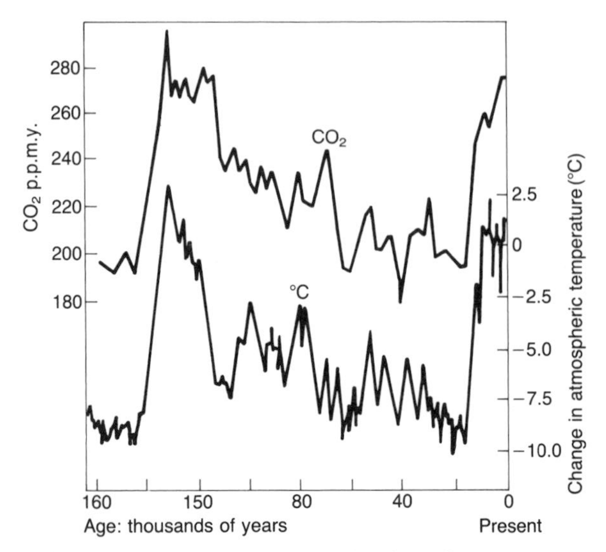

Figure 1.17 Measurements of inferred temperature and carbon dioxide changes for the last 160 000 years from an ice core at Vostok, Antarctica

ii) Clues from ancient air bubbles

Recently, some very exciting information about past climate changes has come from cores of ice drilled in the Antarctic and Greenland ice sheets. Studies of these cores have shown that it is possible to identify tiny bubbles of air, thousands of years old, that are trapped within the ice. Detailed measurements of the composition of the air bubbles has shown the presence of tiny amounts of carbon dioxide (CO_2) and methane gas. The concentrations of these gases have been calculated down individual ice cores spanning the last 160 000 years. The changing CO_2 concentrations mirror estimated changes in global ice volume: the values were very low during past ice ages and very high during periods of global warmth (Figure 1.17). In other words, greenhouse warming was not taking place during the last glaciation, but was very important during the last interglacial. If there was much less CO_2 in the atmosphere during the last ice age, where was the remainder? The answer appears to be that much more CO_2 was stored in the world's oceans. These facts have prompted scientists to pay much more attention to the role that the oceans play in the global CO_2 cycle.

iii) Faunal and floral evidence

a) Faunal changes

The remains of land animals preserved in ancient sediments are often used to provide information on past climate conditions (Figure 1.18). Perhaps the most famous of these are the remains of mammoth that lived in the tundra landscapes of the last ice age. However, it has frequently proved difficult to gather accurate data on past climates from the remains of land animals because of the diversity of environments in which they may have lived.

The remains of insect species have proved more helpful and have provided very detailed information on past climates. The large species diversity and the excellent preservation of their hard parts has resulted in large numbers being preserved within accumulations of sediment. Very common are the remains of beetles. Different beetle species often have quite specific ecological and climatic tolerances. Thus, by knowing the present geographical range of an individual beetle species, it is possible to assess past climate conditions by identifying the remains of particular beetles within a deposit.

b) Pollen analysis and macrofossils

Scientists have learned much about past climates through the study of pollen from seed-bearing plants and the investigation of fossil pollen assemblages (Figure 1.19). Information on past environments has also been gained through the

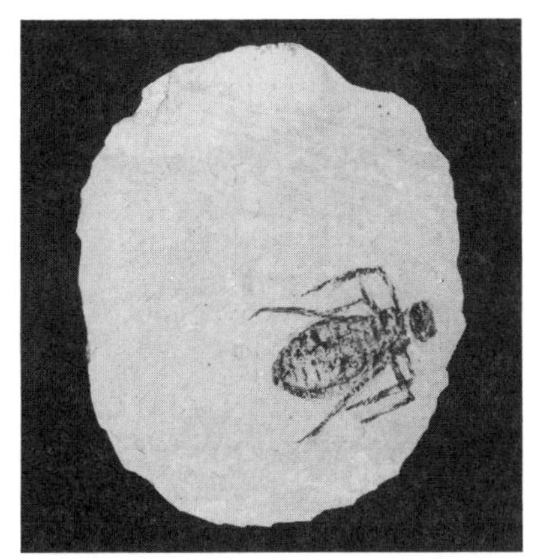

Figure 1.18 *Fossilised insect*

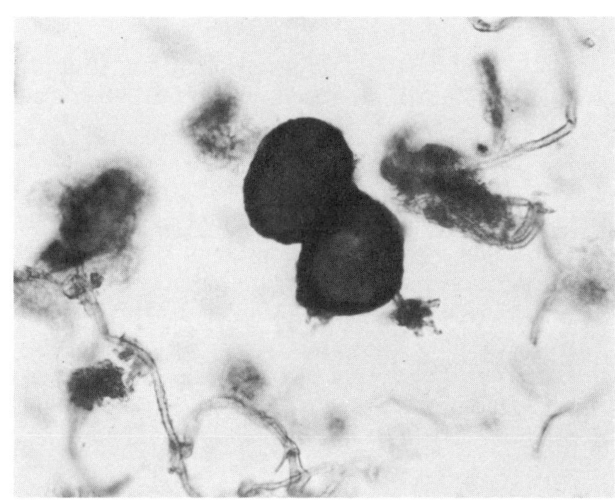

Figure 1.19 *Fossilised pollen grains found in a 6500-year-old peat bog*

Figure 1.20 *Tree rings*

study of larger plant remains (macrofossils) like seeds, fruits, leaves, and tree stumps. Together, this information has enabled the reconstruction of former vegetation patterns. It has also helped scientists to identify the influence of humans as agents of environmental change. The pollen grains are preserved within sediments that have accumulated on the floors of lakes or in peat bogs. Once they are extracted from sediment cores in the laboratory, counts are made of the various species down through the deposit. This painstaking work enables a record of vegetational change over time to be calculated. This is usually depicted in a *pollen diagram.* Thereafter, an attempt is made to estimate former patterns of climate change based on the observed changes in the pollen assemblages.

c) Tree rings

The study of tree rings has provided a very valuable means of reconstructing past climates because climate is the most important factor in tree growth (Figure 1.20). During periods of unfavourable climate, the growth of trees is slowed and a narrow tree ring will result. Conversely, during favourable conditions, the increased rate of growth leads to wider annual tree rings. There are, however, large variations in the development of tree rings between individual species. The most useful are the fir, oak, and pine. In particular, studies of the *Californian bristlecone pine* and oak stumps from Irish peat bogs have enabled detailed reconstructions of past climate variations as far back as 9000 years ago.

The great problem with reconstructing past climates from tree rings (*dendroclimatology*) lies in the identification of those tree ring features that are due to climate and those that are due to other local environmental influences. For example, tree growth is also affected by exposure and changes in soil cover as well as by more subtle changes in soil moisture and the availability of light.

5.2 Short timescales

At a shorter timescale, climatologists study historical records of climates in order to understand patterns of climate change (Table 1.2). Especially useful have been old diaries and written accounts of past weather conditions.

These provide valuable information on past floods, droughts, storms, and snowfalls. Also important have been formal measurements of weather characteristics using meteorological instruments. Considered together, a wealth of information is available that enables scientists to understand more clearly the patterns of past climate changes and their cause.

i) Meteorological records

In 1597, Galileo devised an instrument that measured temperature. Later, in 1643, Torricelli invented a barometer that could measure air pressure. These pioneering achievements were followed in the middle and late seventeenth century by increased interest in patterns of weather and climate. Thus, the first regular series of meteorological measurements began in Florence in 1654. Subsequently, weather measurements were undertaken throughout Europe on a regular basis. In the 1660s, the Royal Society of London began to encourage the recording of weather patterns, but it was not until the mid-eighteenth century that regular weather measurements became established worldwide. For the British Isles, daily weather reports for the period 1873–1980 are available from the Meteorological Office, Bracknell. Monthly weather reports have been kept since 1884.

ii) Diaries and written accounts

The records of past weather conditions from diaries and written accounts extend much farther back in time than those available from meteorological instruments. In these may be found records of daily weather conditions as well as records of extreme events (Figure 1.13). Lamb has pointed out that the written record for lowland Europe is so extensive that every outstanding climatic event since the year 1100 AD has been documented. He has also observed that this is the great shortcoming of old weather records, since their main concern has been with unusual weather. By contrast, there has been much less attention paid to the normal range of weather during past decades and centuries.

One of the biggest problems in reconstructing past weather patterns is the lack of data for the world's oceans. For example, the first measurements of sea surface temperatures only began in the 1780s. The records of ocean weather are available from ships' log books. These have often provided very valuable information about the direction and speed of the prevailing winds. Despite the great importance of the records of past weather from the oceans, the data are very sparse when compared to that available from the land.

5.3 Predicting future climates

Despite the enormous amount of information on past climates now available, scientists have discovered that the task of accurate climate prediction is still as elusive as ever. In Britain, a dramatic example of this was the great storm of 17th October 1987 that devastated large areas of southern England and which took meteorologists by surprise. Similarly, meteorologists have great difficulty in predicting the paths of hurricanes. For example, it proved almost impossible to predict the likely track of *Hurricane Hugo* across the Caribbean and south-eastern USA during September 1989. Inhabitants on the islands of Montserrat and Guadeloupe, where nearly every home was destroyed, had no more than 12–24 hours warning that they were likely to experience a *direct hit* from the hurricane.

In Part II, an attempt is made to summarise the most important trends in climate that are now known to have taken place in the recent geological past as well as during the historical time period. The list of changes should not be considered exhaustive. Instead, an attempt is made to highlight the most important changes that have taken place and to consider the changes in terms of what might take place on earth in the future.

Part II
TIMESCALES OF CLIMATE CHANGE

1 THE QUATERNARY ICE AGE

1.1 Introduction

The Quaternary Period was once regarded as the *Great Ice Age*. However, more recent evidence suggests that there were many periods of glaciation (*glacials*) separated by periods of warmth (*interglacials*) during the Quaternary Ice Age. The beginning of the Quaternary Ice Age is difficult to define, especially when we consider that glaciers perhaps started to form over Antarctica 37 million years ago. The generally held view is that the beginning of the Quaternary coincides with the time when plant and animal fossils in rocks indicate the start of a pronounced worldwide cooling considerably more severe than any that took place during the preceding Tertiary Period. Accordingly, the beginning of the Quaternary corresponds to the time when ice sheets first developed in the middle latitudes of the northern hemisphere. Most estimates place the timing of this worldwide cooling between 1.6 and 2.4 million years ago.

The oxygen isotope curves show that immense ice sheets built up on seventeen or as many as twenty-two separate occasions during the whole Quaternary. Surprisingly, the periods of intervening interglacial warmth appear to have been relatively short. The curves, however, are ominous for humankind since they show that many of the changeovers from glacial cold to interglacial warmth, and vice versa, were very rapid.

The curves also show that we are living in the most recent period of interglacial warmth. However, if we look at the curves more closely, it is clear that there have been very few periods of time during the Quaternary when global climate has been as warm as it is at present. Indeed, a global climate as warm as today's may have existed for just 5 per cent of the total time-span of the last 2 million years. On a geological timescale, we are living in an unusually warm period. For most of the last 2–3 million years, glacial conditions have existed in the northern hemisphere. Civilisation has, therefore, inherited the earth at an opportune time.

The global changes in climate that have taken place during the last 1 million years are of much greater magnitude than those that took place during earlier geological history. Inspection of the curve in Figure 1.14a shows that it has a *saw-tooth* character which illustrates that drastic and rapid climate changes have taken place. It also shows that during the later part of the Quaternary there may have been at least eleven major ice ages, during which colossal ice sheets developed over North America, North-West Europe, and Russia. The Antarctic and Greenland ice sheets probably existed for most of this period despite fluctuating somewhat in size. A very important exception is the West Antarctic ice sheet which may have disintegrated during the last interglacial.

Many scientists have observed that there is a close fit between the oxygen isotope curves and the Milankovitch curves that show the long-term variations in the amount of heat distributed over the earth's surface (Figure 1.11). This has led to the suggestion that the Milankovitch Cycles represent the *Pacemaker of the Ice Ages*. A particularly interesting aspect of the Milankovitch curves is that the 96000, 41000, and 23000-year cycles are notable trends which can also be recognised in the oxygen isotope curves for the last 1 million years. The correlations are poorer, however, for earlier time periods. Some have even argued that the eccentricity cycle is not evident in ocean sediments older than 1 million years and that we must look for other explanations for the climate changes that took place during the earlier part of the Quaternary.

1.2 The last Ice Age

The last Ice Age culminated about 18 000 years ago when immense ice sheets were again produced over wide areas of the earth's surface. In North America, the enormous *Laurentide ice sheet* extended as far south as the Great Lakes. It spanned the entire continent from east to west and reached a maximum thickness of nearly 3000 m. A separate ice sheet developed over western Canada and southern Alaska. In Europe, much of Britain was overwhelmed by ice, while a large ice sheet covered most of Norway, Sweden, Finland, European Russia, and Siberia. Elsewhere, smaller ice masses were produced in such unlikely places as southern New Zealand, Patagonia, the Pyrenees, Venezuela, and the highlands of Papua New Guinea. The growth of glaciers and ice sheets also led to a worldwide fall in sea-level of almost 120 m.

i) Ice Age lakes

At lower latitudes, decreased evaporation and lower temperatures led to increases in the size of many lakes. One of the largest, Lake Bonneville, was created in the western USA where it reached a maximum area of 300 000 km^2. Due to climate change the lake is now dry and its floor covered by the famous Bonneville salt flats. Similarly, Death Valley 18 000 years ago received considerable quantities of meltwater draining from glaciers in the Sierra Nevada mountains. In Africa, a large lake covered much of Chad and many other lakes were produced over Northern Africa and in the East African Rift Valley. In the Middle East, large lakes were formed in what is now the Lake Tiberias (Sea of Galilee) area.

The largest lakes, however, were produced along the southern margins of the northern hemisphere ice sheets. In the lowlands of western Siberia an enormous lake covering more than 1 million km^2 was produced. Overflow from the lake took place into the Aral and Caspian Seas and eventually into the Black Sea, from where the glacial meltwaters drained into the eastern Mediterranean. Gigantic lakes were also dammed along the southern margin of the North American ice sheet. The largest of these was *Glacial Lake Agassiz*, the overflow from which drained southwards along the Minnesota and Mississippi Valleys, into the Gulf of Mexico. Later, as the ice sheet thinned and shrank in size, the overflow waters from the lake drained eastwards into the North Atlantic. It is thought that the reorganisation of water circulation at this time, particularly the sudden supply of freshwater into the North Atlantic, may have led to dramatic climate changes across the northern hemisphere. This may have been initiated by the major reduction in the salinity of the surface waters of the North Atlantic, so causing widespread cooling.

ii) Ice Age oceans

The Ice Age Arctic Ocean and North Atlantic had a more extensive cover of sea ice than at present. Indeed, during winters, there was an almost continuous sea ice cover as far south as the latitude of southern Spain and New York. Consequently, there was no Gulf Stream in the North Atlantic. The cover of sea ice prevented evaporation of moisture from the ocean surface and led to the development of high pressure in the atmosphere. High pressure and anticyclonic conditions also existed over the huge ice sheets on neighbouring continents. As a result of these processes, the Arctic Ocean and neighbouring landmasses were starved of precipitation. Areas of northern Britain and the present northern North Sea were dry land due to the combined influence of aridity and sea-level lowering (Figure 2.1).

In the southern hemisphere, the cover of sea ice was greatly increased and caused substantial changes in the climate of neighbouring continents. In the North Pacific, floating ice shelves extended many kilometres offshore from southern Alaska and western Canada. These changes were accompanied by an anchoring of large cells of high pressure (anticyclones) over the world's major oceans. In some ocean areas (notably near the Galapagos Islands and Easter Island in the eastern Pacific) this process caused ocean temperatures to be warmer (by 1°C) during the last Ice Age than they are at present. Ice Age conditions were not so pleasant along the western margins of continents where, due to stronger upwelling currents caused by the anticyclones, the coastal deserts greatly increased in size. In the Atacama region of western Chile and in the desert areas of South-West and North-West Africa, for example, there was widespread desertification.

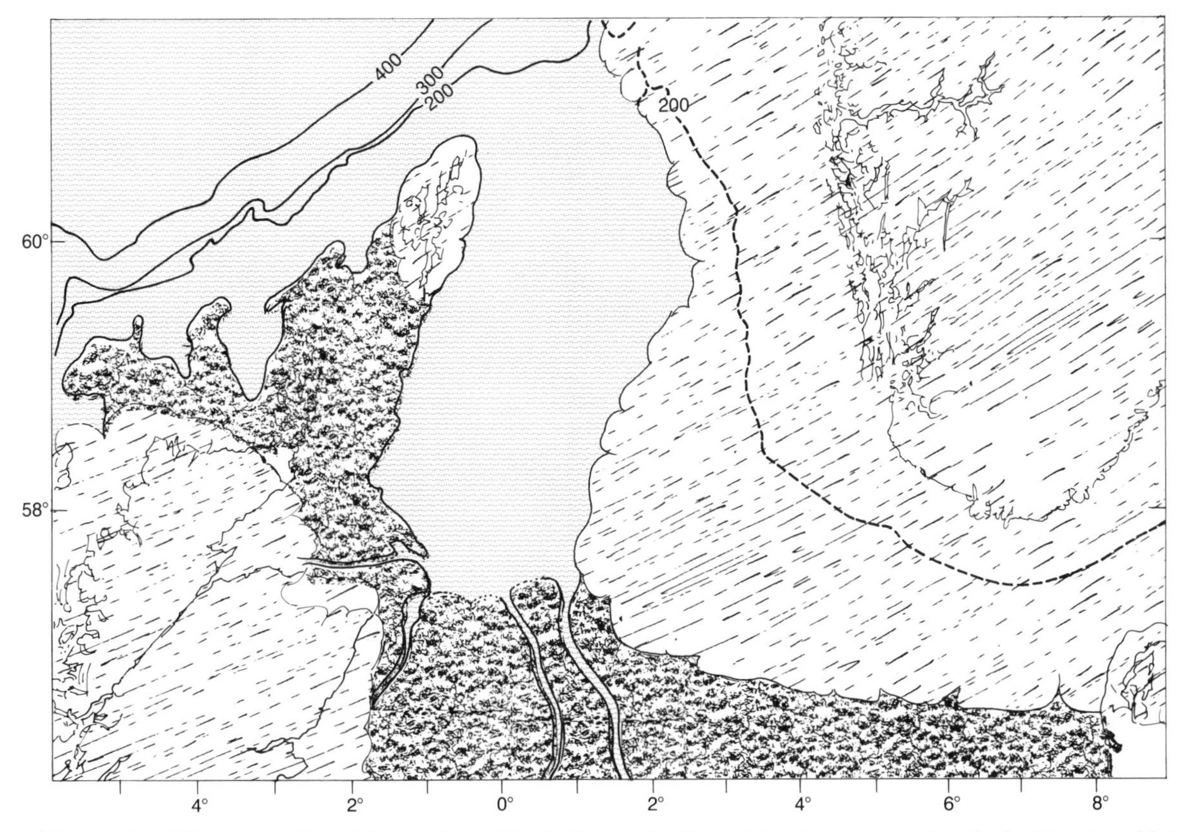

Figure 2.1 The geography of the northern North Sea and adjacent landmasses during the last Ice Age. Note the large areas of the present North Sea that were areas of dry land at that time due to sea-level lowering and absence of glacier ice

iii) Ice Age atmospheric and oceanic circulation

The creation of large ice sheets in the northern hemisphere during the last Ice Age resulted in major changes in global atmospheric and oceanic circulation. For example, the great size and thickness of the ice sheets caused the jet streams in the upper atmosphere to become diverted around the ice masses. In addition, the cold surfaces of the ice sheets caused a continued cooling, and hence sinking, of the air masses above their surfaces. The flow of the jet streams was significantly different from their present path with the splitting of the westerly mid-latitude jet to the north and south of the North American and Eurasian ice sheets. Over the Asian continent, the high pressure created above the Eurasian ice sheet also resulted in dramatic changes in the mechanics of the Asian monsoon. The high pressure effectively blocked the invasion of monsoon precipitation and caused vast areas of the Indian subcontinent to become desert.

During this period, the world's climatic belts were also radically displaced. Thus, the rain-bearing mid-latitude westerlies were steered south of the ice sheets, and this resulted in increased rainfall over south-western USA and the Mediterranean. Similarly, the subtropical anticyclones were displaced equatorwards, and this led to the development of deserts at latitudes quite different from those of today. For example, dune fields were produced in parts of the Amazon Basin while the Kalahari Desert occupied a greatly increased area of Southern Africa. There was also a change in the location of the desert

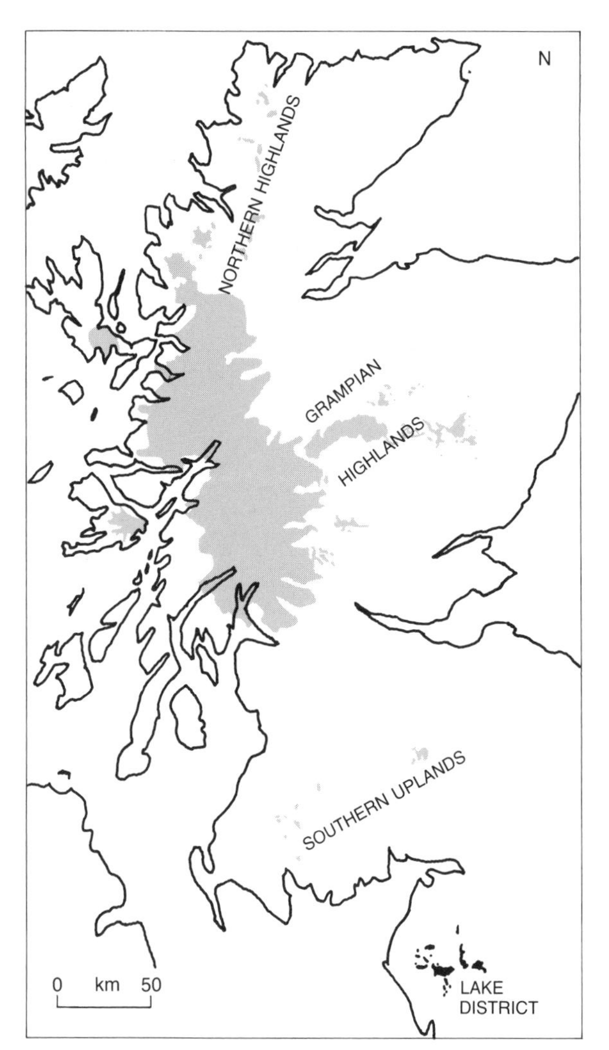

Figure 2.2 *Distribution of glaciers in Scotland during the cold climate of the Younger Dryas*

areas of North Africa. In the tropics, increased aridity lead to the disappearance of most areas of tropical rainforest.

The lowering of temperatures also led to the development of vast areas of tundra. Cold-climate periglacial conditions were characteristic of huge areas of central North America and the European steppe. Microscopic rock fragments eroded by the ice sheets and transported by rivers were eventually deposited by wind processes across wide areas. In China, these wind-blown deposits, known as *loess*, were extensively deposited. In certain parts of China, loess deposition throughout the Quaternary led to the accumulation of sediments up to 300 m thick. Loess deposition was also widespread elsewhere, with considerable thicknesses of silt being deposited over the North European Plain and across wide areas of the USA.

iv) The Younger Dryas glaciation

The end of the last Ice Age was interrupted on several occasions by the renewed growth of glacier ice. The most notable phase took place approximately 11 000 years ago when a widespread global cooling led to the rapid growth of glacier ice. The period of cooling seems to have lasted for several hundred years and was of sufficient magnitude and rapidity to serve as a reminder that global climatic deteriorations can happen quite suddenly. This period, known as the *Younger Dryas* cold period, is sometimes thought of as a *failed glaciation*, because no sooner had it started than it ended.

The environmental consequences of the Younger Dryas cooling were particularly severe in North-West Europe. In southern England, for example, the mean July temperature was little more than 10°C, while mean January temperatures may have frequently plunged to −20°C. As many as sixty-four valley glaciers were produced in the English Lake District and a major ice cap was formed over the western Highlands of Scotland (Figure 2.2). By contrast, relatively few glaciers were produced in the Cairngorms of Scotland. This is surprising since this area is at present a popular skiing centre and the first to receive snowfall in winter. However, conditions during the Younger Dryas were very different. The easterly winds were relatively dry and deficient in snow because, due to sea-level lowering, most of the present North Sea area was dry land.

2 CLIMATE AFTER THE ICE AGES

2.1 Trends in global warming and cooling

The climatic warming that commenced at the end of the last Ice Age represented the start of a warming trend that has essentially continued to the present day. However, brief periods of global cooling have interrupted this overall warming. When we examine the climate changes that have taken place over the last 10000 years (the Holocene) we find evidence that they have been extremely complex (Figure 2.3). During the early part of the Holocene, there was a progressive warming throughout the northern hemisphere. The warming was very pronounced and may even have reached values higher than present between 8000 and 6000 years ago. This period of enhanced warmth may even have been associated with sea-levels slightly higher than present, since the higher temperatures may have caused accelerated melting of ice in Antarctica. Thereafter, global climate appears to have become cooler and moister. This period, known as the *Neoglacial* period, seems to have been characterised by marked fluctuations of Alpine glaciers, something that is indicative of alternating periods of cooling and warming. The principal periods of ice advance, and hence climatic deterioration, appear to have been centred on 5800–4900 years ago, 3300–2400 years ago, and 1200–1000 years ago, as well as a more recent marked global cooling that culminated during the eighteenth and nineteenth centuries. This period of cool climate, known as the *Little Ice Age*, spanned the time period between approximately 1300 and 1900 AD (Figure 2.3).

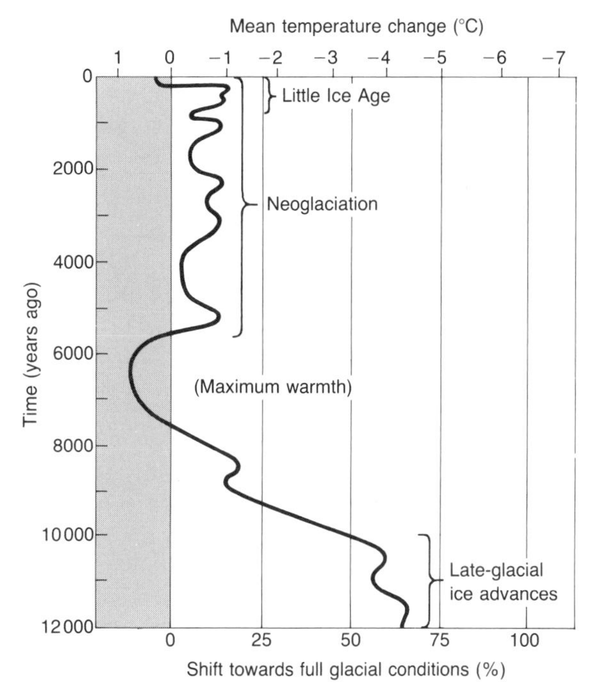

Figure 2.3 *Generalised curve of temperature changes in the northern hemisphere for the last 12000 years*

2.2 Climate changes during recent centuries

i) The Little Ice Age

Despite a brief interlude of climate warming between 1500 and 1550 AD, the trend of climatic cooling accelerated during the middle of the sixteenth century. The cooling was particularly pronounced between 1550 and 1700 and corresponded to a period of time when worldwide cooling was registered (Figure 2.4). Detailed information on the climate changes that took place are evident from ice cores taken in Greenland. Very careful studies have shown that there is a good correspondence between inferred temperatures and variations in the acidity of the ice. High acidity values are caused by the fall-out of volcanic sulphate aerosols from the atmosphere. It appears that periods of higher-than-average temperatures in the northern hemisphere occur when there is very little volcanic activity.

The Greenland ice core studies have shown that a pronounced lowering of temperature took place between approximately 1300 and 1900AD, the period known as the *Little Ice Age* (Figure 2.4). In Europe, the Little Ice Age was marked by relatively snowy winters and cool, wet, and short summers that led to a pronounced advance of many Alpine glaciers and the well-known *frost fairs* on the River Thames (Figure 2.5). During the peak of the Little Ice Age, average annual air temperatures may have been more than 1°C

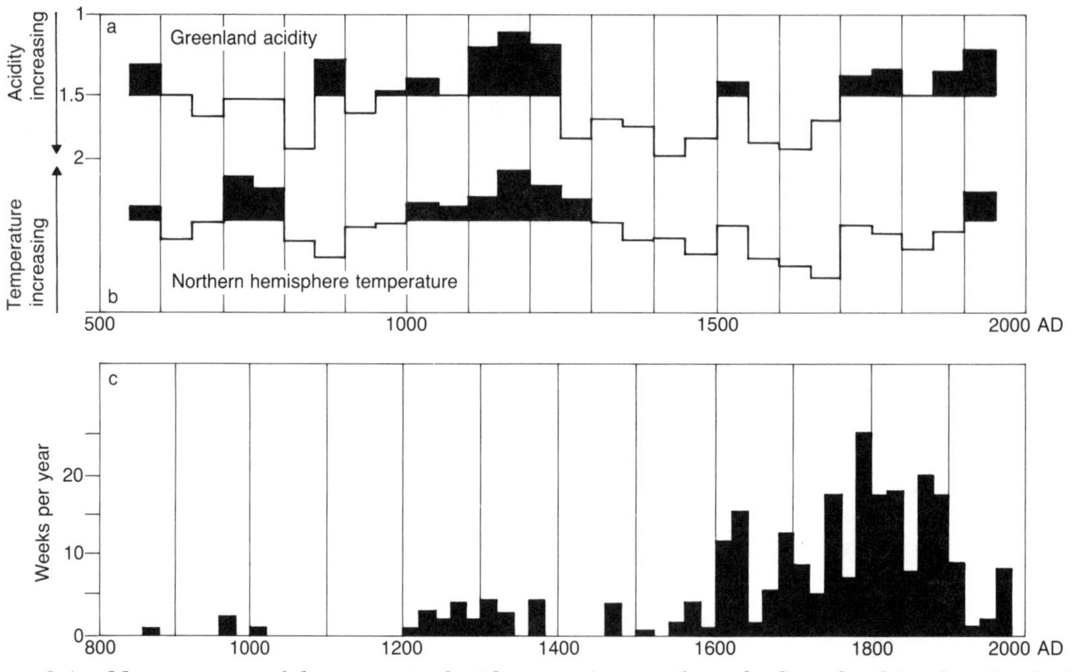

Figure 2.4 **a** *Measurements of the amounts of acid present in cores from the Greenland ice sheet for the last 1500 years. Periods of increased acidity are thought to equate with periods of volcanic activity.* **b** *Trend of northern hemisphere temperature for the last 1500 years. Note that periods of low acidity appear to correlate with periods of higher-than-average temperatures.* **c** *Variations in the occurrence of sea ice around the coasts of Iceland for the last 1200 years. The greatest occurrence of sea ice corresponds with the occurrence of the Little Ice Age*

cooler than at present. In the North Atlantic, the southern limit of winter sea ice extended south of Iceland (Figure 2.4). The Greenland settlements first established by Erik the Red in 985 AD endured the regional deterioration in climate until approximately 1420 AD when they were abandoned, largely due to the severe cold.

Most of North-West Europe was affected by lower temperatures. In England, average annual temperatures during the late seventeenth century were approximately 0.9°C lower than they were between 1920 and 1960. In the North Atlantic, there was a considerable increase in sea ice cover, with ocean temperatures between the Faroes and Iceland in the period 1675–1705 being nearly 5°C colder than at present. In Iceland, the worst year was 1695 when the island was almost entirely 'landlocked' by sea ice. Indeed, Professor Lamb describes a remarkable occasion when an Eskimo, having drifted on an ice floe, arrived in a kayak in the Don Estuary in Aberdeen! In Europe, the severe winters of the Little Ice Age are depicted in the paintings of Breugel (some of which are often used as illustrations for Christmas cards). During the winter of 1683–84, a 5 km-wide belt of sea ice developed along the Channel coasts of south-eastern England and northern France. In the last decade of the seventeenth century, Scotland was racked by a tragic famine caused largely by repeated crop failure due to a series of brief, wet summers and long and bitterly cold winters. The famine played a large part in the political manoeuvering that finally led to the Union of the Scottish and English parliaments in January 1707. Episodes of severe storminess also appear to have been a characteristic of the Little Ice Age. For example, particularly stormy weather affected many coastal areas of North-West Europe during the 1590s, 1690s, and 1790s.

Figure 2.5 *A Frost Fair on the River Thames, 1684*

In many areas, the Little Ice Age appears to have been characterised by a much greater variability in climate, with particularly marked fluctuations in rainfall. For example, there were many highly damaging floods and droughts in West Africa between 1550 and 1750, while in India the monsoon rains failed on numerous occasions. There was a pronounced period of early warming between 1730 and 1750, although one of the worst winters on record occurred during 1708–09. Severe summer droughts occurred in England during 1718 and 1719. Dramatic fluctuations are also indicated by the bitterly cold winters that occurred between 1769 and 1771 and the series of very wet summers that spanned the period between 1751 and 1784. Professor Lamb has also drawn attention to a series of very stormy winters between 1790 and 1800 when wind gusts occasionally exceeded 160 mph, causing particularly severe damage in many coastal communities. Probably the greatest storm, however, took place in December 1703 when a hurricane that tracked across southern Britain caused widespread damage and led to the death of 8000 people.

ii) Climate fluctuations during the nineteenth and twentieth centuries

Drastic fluctuations in climate continued throughout the nineteenth century. For example, severe droughts occurred in England during the summers of 1826, 1846, and 1868. In contrast to this, there were occasional very cold winters. Many of the winters in the early life of Charles Dickens (between 1812 and 1820) may have led to Dickens' vivid descriptions of *white Christmasses*. In general, the mild conditions of the mid-nineteenth century were followed by a return to colder conditions at the end of the century. Between 1875 and 1900, many years were characterised by cold snowy winters and short, cool, and wet summers.

At the end of the nineteenth century the climate changed for the better (Figure 2.4). The winter of 1894–95 was one of the last when ice formed on the River Thames. Between 1900 and 1950 there was a steady and almost uninterrupted increase in the average temperature of both the northern and southern hemispheres. This period was the most abnormal of the past thousand years since the rise in temperature

worldwide was sustained for several decades. Throughout this period there was a high frequency of westerly winds over Britain and this led to mild winters and warmer springs. In 1933, the permanent snowbed that had existed on the north-facing cliffs of Ben Nevis since at least 1840 finally disappeared. Many people remember the warm summers that preceded the outbreak of World War II. Since 1950, however, there has been a tendency for summers to become cooler and for greater variability in climatic extremes. Very severe winters occurred during 1940, 1947, and 1963. Taking into account temperature, rainfall, and snowfall, there seems to have been an increase in the frequency of climate extremes.

The significance of the climate changes that have taken place during the last 100 years are particularly difficult to interpret since we need to distinguish those changes attributable to human activities from those due to other causes. It is this unresolved question that remains as one of the most challenging for humankind in the future.

2.3 Climate during recent decades

The trends in global climate change for the last few decades present a very confusing picture. One view is that a global cooling trend started during the 1950s and has continued, essentially unhindered, until the present day. However, it is almost impossible to identify a period of global cooling at any one moment in time and label it as a cooling episode that will trigger the next ice age. The contrasting view is that the build-up of carbon dioxide in the atmosphere is leading to *overheating* and that climate warming (and sea-level rise) is taking place in response to human activity. These issues are further complicated by the climate cooling that took place in the northern hemisphere during the latter part of 1988 and the first months of 1989. This appears to have been related to vigorous wind and water circulation in the tropical Pacific (see below).

i) The influence of changes in jet stream flow

During the first half of this century, the path of the mid-latitude jet stream did not vary much and was characterised by a streamlined west to east air flow. As a result, the westerly cyclones in the North Atlantic tended to track in similar directions. In Britain, this led to few extremes of temperature, with the cyclones bringing a regular supply of rainfall. This pattern of vigorous air circulation also led to few climatic extremes in North America, while in the North Atlantic sea surface temperatures did not fluctuate to any great degree.

By contrast, the years between 1950 and 1980 were characterised by a slight global cooling which was accompanied by a weakening of jet stream flow in the upper troposphere. This caused a sluggish pattern of jet stream flow in which a standing jet stream wave developed across the northern hemisphere. This, in turn, led to much greater extremes of climate, with many more severe winters and summers characterised by drought.

The most extreme conditions occurred when several high amplitude jet stream waves were produced. For example, the severe drought of 1976 was accompanied by blocking circulation that led to the establishment of a warm anti-cyclone over most of the British landmass. Similar conditions were associated with the summer drought of 1989 in Britain. As a result of the blocking, cyclones in the North Atlantic were steered around the anticyclone and this led to relatively high precipitation in surrounding regions. Thus, the drought of 1976 was associated with considerable rainfall over Iceland and northern Scotland and higher-than-average rainfall over Spain and France.

ii) The influence of El Nino and La Nina

Scientists have observed that there was a marked global cooling during the latter part of 1988 and during 1989. This cooling followed a conspicuous warming phase during early and mid-1988 when global temperatures were approximately 0.35°C warmer than the average value for the three decades between 1950 and 1980. The phases of cooling and warming have been mostly attributed to the effects of *El Nino* and *La Nina* – climatic events that occur in the tropical Pacific when the east to west ocean and wind currents are subject to sudden changes (Figure 2.6). El Nino is Spanish for 'Christ Child' or 'the little boy' because it usually occurs in the eastern Pacific around Christmas. La Nina is Spanish for 'the little girl', so-called because it is the opposite of El Nino.

When an El Nino event takes place, there is an

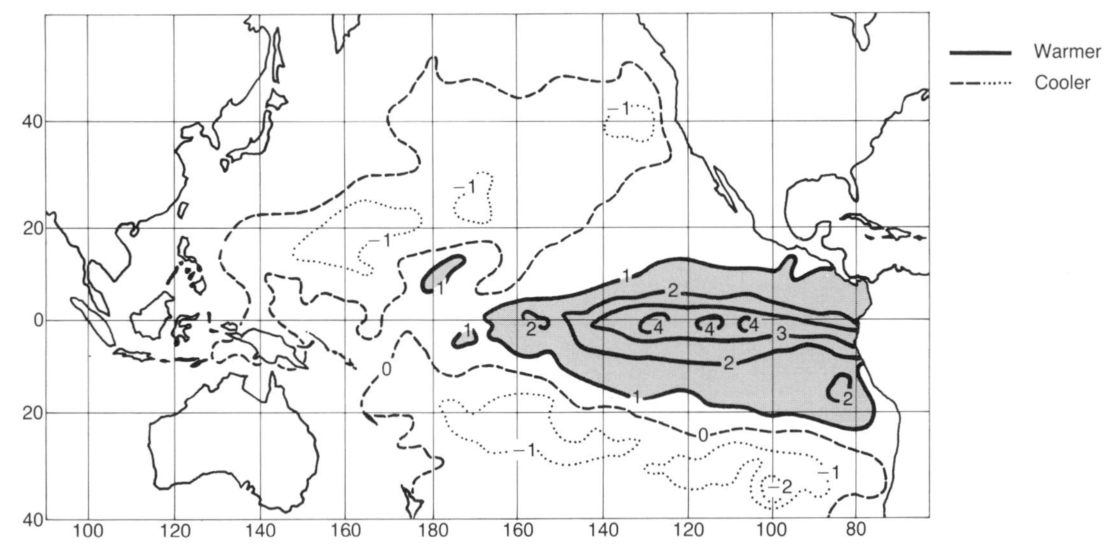

Figure 2.6 *The observed pattern of sea surface temperature anomalies in the Pacific Ocean associated with the El Nino event of December 1982*

Figure 2.7 *The aftermath of a storm in California, March 1983. The storm was associated with an El Nino event in the Pacific Ocean*

over-heating of the tropical Pacific Ocean and a reversal of the flow of water and air currents. When this happens, the normally arid coasts of South America are subject to periods of heavy rainfall. An El Nino event also seems to trigger abnormal rainfall in other parts of the world. It may cause the failure of the Indian monsoon as well as drought throughout many areas of East Africa, Indonesia, and northern Australia.

By contrast, La Nina is characterised by a substantial increase in the vigour of the prevailing winds and currents in the tropical Pacific, and this causes a marked cooling of the surface waters. A marked La Nina cooling during 1988 may have led to global cooling.

Some scientists believe that El Nino and La Nina events are closely related to the greenhouse effect. The warming of the surface waters of the tropical Pacific may be triggering a series of El Nino events in an unpredictable manner. It is possible that La Nina events may counterbalance El Nino outbreaks. If only a few La Nina events occur, the net effect may be to exaggerate the effects of greenhouse warming. If El Nino is related to greenhouse effects, one might expect the remainder of the twentieth century to be characterised by a series of El Nino and La Nina temperature fluctuations that are difficult to distinguish from other elements of the temperature equation.

3 PRESENT TRENDS AND FUTURE PROSPECTS

3.1 Perspectives on past climates

At present we are living in one of the relatively few periods of interglacial warmth that have occurred over the last 2 million years. Within the timescale of the present interglacial, we are living in one of its warmest periods. Indeed, our present climate is abnormally warm when compared with the climate of the past thousand years. If we are to believe the Milankovitch Cycles, then it is likely that humankind is presently living at the end of an interglacial period. If we are to enter a glacial period, how soon will it be before the change takes place?

When we consider past fluctuations in climate, it is clear that many took place extremely rapidly. How, therefore, can we predict which way global climate will turn? Most probably, the patterns of climate change in the near future will be driven by unpredicted events. For example, there may be a major volcanic eruption about to take place that will cause global cooling during the remaining years of this century. Less likely, but in no way impossible, is the occurrence of a future climatic deterioration due to a major meteorite impact. It is not a very pleasant event to contemplate, let alone model! It is important to be aware, however, that climate can fluctuate from interglacial warmth to glacial cold very quickly.

The occurrence of the Younger Dryas period of cold climate is of great relevance to the future of humankind since it demonstrates that global climate can switch from warmth to severe cold very quickly, perhaps as quickly as a matter of decades. Is it possible, for example, that the climate of southern England could switch to a tundra regime within a matter of years? Might it therefore be appropriate to consider that the Younger Dryas represents an example of *instantaneous glaciation*? For these reasons, it is essential to understand the climatic mechanisms that triggered the onset of the Younger Dryas. At present, large sums of money are being spent in the search for answers to this question. If it proves to be the case that the Younger Dryas cooling was inextricably linked to the melting of the last ice sheets in the middle latitudes, we may perhaps have little to worry about. However, if the Younger Dryas cooling was triggered by exceptional volcanism, or some other external cause, we may not be so certain that such an event might not happen again.

It is also possible that future climate may be characterised by a pronounced warming. Such warming may be driven, for example, by *greenhouse* processes, by another El Nino event, or by solar flaring. In this regard, a key issue is whether the rise in ocean temperatures around

Antarctica would be sufficient to trigger the disintegration of the ice shelves that border the West Antarctic ice sheet. Disintegration of the ice sheet due to this process is a vital factor that will largely dictate the pattern of future sea-level changes around the world.

3.2 Where do we go from here?

Despite the enormous scientific advances that have been made in recent years, we are still a long way away from understanding how the earth's climate system operates. We do not know, for example, if the development of an *ozone hole* over Antarctica during spring is a *natural* process or if it is directly attributable to human activities. Similarly, we are not yet in a position to understand the way in which oceans influence changes in global atmospheric circulation. We still have a great deal to learn about the greenhouse effect. It is vital to quantify the processes that appear to be taking place. We are only beginning to learn about El Nino and La Nina and we do not yet understand the ways in which volcanic eruptions influence climate. We are only beginning to understand solar flaring episodes. It is thus very difficult, for example, to distinguish the climatic warming effects of El Nino events, the greenhouse effect, and solar flaring. These are only some of the unsolved climatic questions. Part of the reason why they have not been answered is that the detailed analytical techniques and sophisticated methods of dating former environmental changes have only been mastered in recent years. Thus, the period of time for which detailed information is available is relatively short.

During 1988, the world was warmer than at any time since meteorological records began. Some scientists have observed that the six warmest years this century have all been in the 1980s. Despite the observed cooling that took place during late 1988 and 1989, one might argue from this that global warming is the dominant trend and that it has arisen due to the combined influence of the enhanced greenhouse effect and people-made pollution. The key question, which is difficult to answer, is whether or not the massive injections of carbon dioxide and methane gases into the atmosphere may be creating a greenhouse effect that is of sufficient magnitude to counter any trend towards a new glacial age. Unfortunately, the natural causes of global temperature fluctuation are still so poorly understood that it is proving almost impossible to assess the degree to which the global changes are human-induced. The provision of answers to these issues is made infinitely more difficult by the fact that it is now clear from solar flare measurements that the earth does not receive a constant amount of heat from the sun. The complex nature of atmospheric processes is also well-illustrated by the controversy over the causal factors behind the great storms of January and February 1990. It is not yet clear if North-West Europe is witnessing a new cycle of storminess similar to those that occurred during the Little Ice Age or if the storms represent an indirect product of greenhouse warming.

The problems described above need rapid solutions. Scientists have been able to measure in Arctic snow concentrations of lead that are derived from vehicle exhaust emissions in the great cities of the northern hemisphere. The explorer, Robert Swan, has depressingly described the *Arctic haze* air pollution in the lower troposphere. Similarly, the acid rain of North-West Europe is a testament to the massive pumping of chemical waste into the lower atmosphere. The list of human destructive influences on global climate is almost endless. For those who are aware of their environment and the way that it is changing, the wise words of politicians are of little comfort since there does not seem to be a serious attempt by the international community to effect any changes. In this respect, increased public awareness of the ways in which our climate works is essential if we are to rescue our planet.

Part III
EXERCISES

1 THE OZONE LAYER

Study Figure 3.1a and b.

i) Why is October an important month to measure ozone concentrations over Antarctica?
ii) Does the data indicate that ozone depletion is restricted to Antarctica or has a decrease taken place worldwide in recent years?
iii) Describe the trends in ozone concentrations that are evident in Figure 3.1a.
iv) Are the same trends indicated from the global satellite data in Figure 3.1b?

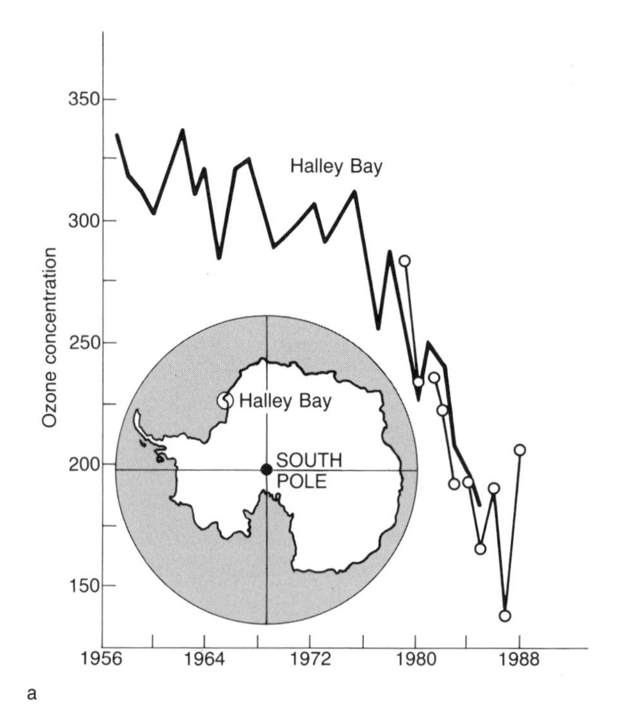

Figure 3.1 **a** *Average ozone concentration above Halley Bay, Antarctica, during October each year since 1956.* **b** *Average global ozone concentrations between 1979 and 1986*

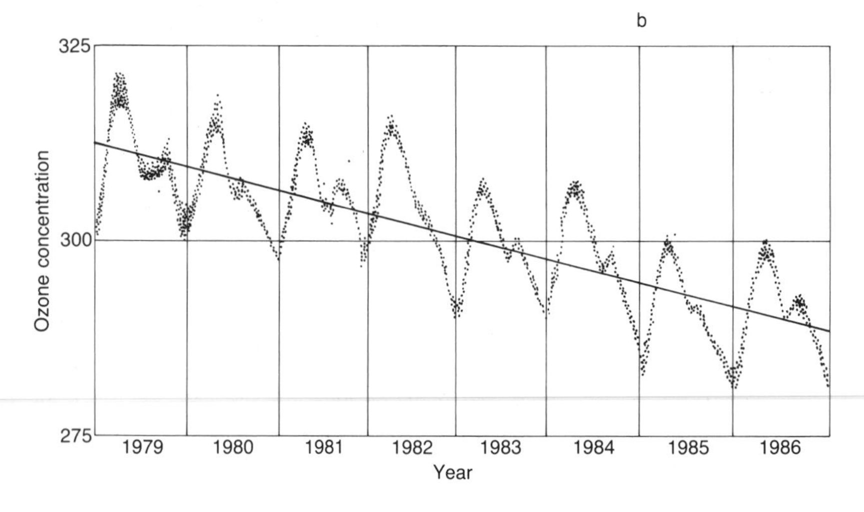

Study Table 3.1. It shows the projected number of cases of skin cancer induced by a thinning of the ozone layer.

i) Plot on a graph the number of cases of skin cancer when no control taken (vertical axis) against time (horizontal axis).
ii) Plot on the same graph the number of cases that are likely with a freeze introduced in 1990 on the emission of ozone-damaging gases.
iii) Suggest why the incidence of skin cancer has increased with depletion of the ozone layer.
iv) What effect is likely if there is an emissions freeze?

Table 3.1 Projected number of skin cancer victims in the USA caused by depletion of the ozone layer

Year	*Cases (000s) when no control taken*	*Cases (000s) with freeze on emissions*
1980	5	–
1985	8	–
1990	16	16
1995	36	24
2000	40	28
2005	60	36
2010	72	42
2015	116	49
2020	156	56

2 GLOBAL WARMING

The issue of global warming is now perceived as one of immense importance. Not surprisingly, the issue has led to great political controversy at both local, national, and international levels.

This exercise involves a simple role-playing game. You should undertake the exercise in small groups, with each group taking a separate role (Table 3.2 on page 46).

Scenario. An international debate is being held at the United Nations to discuss the issue of global warming. The debate has been carefully organised so that as many interested organisations as possible can attend and present their views. Likely concerns are future sea-level rise, anticipated shifts in global weather patterns, destruction of the tropical rainforest, greater storminess, injection of greenhouse gases into the atmosphere, burning of fossil fuels, and accelerated melting of the world's ice sheets.

i) Your task is to prepare a set of policy measures which, if implemented by governments, would slow down the rate of global warming. It is very difficult to prepare a document that will find general favour. Different organisations have often very different views about what measures should be taken. In this exercise, five organisations have been asked to form a committee to consider what measures might usefully be taken to counter the processes of global warming. The conclusions that they draw will be presented for discussion before the General Assembly of the United Nations.

ii) Appoint a chairperson. Also appoint a spokesperson for each delegation. The duty of the chairperson is to preside over a discussion between the six spokespersons. This person should direct the discussion and should draw attention to important issues that arise from the discussion.

iii) Acting out your roles, identify a strategy for your group. Also define a series of objectives that you hope to gain from the discussion. Consider some statements of policy that might be acceptable to the other groups. Remember also that you will have some political allies at the final United Nations debate. Consider how they are likely to respond to your suggestions.

The President of Brazil and delegation

You represent a country in the developing world that possesses one of the world's largest areas of tropical rainforest. You are under a great deal of pressure from Western governments who are very concerned about the rate at which areas of the Amazon rainforest are being cleared. They have hinted to you that they might demand some repayment of international loans unless you do something to halt the destruction of the rainforest. However, you are also under pressure from within your own country, especially from those who maintain that the development of the Amazon Basin is fundamental to the economic prosperity of Brazil.

The President of Italy and delegation

You represent a member state of the EC. You have a particular crisis at the moment since the future of the city of Venice is under threat from global sea-level rise. Geologists and engineers have provided reports that conclude that most of the city will be completely submerged by 2030 AD provided that the anticipated increases in global sea-level prove to be correct. The Italian public wish to see evidence that some measures are actively being taken to save the city from flooding. You are therefore under pressure to support measures which counteract the processes of global warming.

The President of the USA and delegation

You represent one of the most important industrialised powers in the world. You are under pressure from many sources. One of the most politically sensitive issues is the nation's energy policy. On the one hand, business interests urge you that the most efficient solution is to build a large number of nuclear power stations. On the other hand, the public and the media are strongly opposed to nuclear power. Yet, of the various energy sources, nuclear power appears the least likely to contribute to global warming. You are also anxious to keep the US business lobby happy. They are presently investing a great deal in South America, especially in Brazil.

President of Friends of the Earth and delegation

You represent a very influential pressure group that has a worldwide membership. Your main interest is to ensure that the policy statement is a positive and forward-looking document. You are very aware that government leaders might attempt to outline a series of measures that will lead to little change. You believe that you can influence particular governments by pointing to individual issues (for example, increased car production) in which governments appear to be at fault. You consider various forms of protest action that you might be prepared to implement.

President of Mauritania and delegation

You represent one of the poorest countries in Africa. Scientists have told you that global warming and shifts in the climatic belts might partly be responsible for the increasing number of droughts in your country. Your country owes a great deal of interest on loans that are due for payment to several Western governments (including the USA). You wish to undertake extensive drilling for possible groundwater sources. Yet this is very expensive and you are having difficulty in securing more loans. You feel resentful to Western governments since you believe they are largely responsible for the global warming that has led to drought in your country.

Prime Minister of the UK and delegation

You represent a country closely allied to the USA. You are under pressure to maintain a green image. Business interests urge you to increase timber imports from Brazil, much to the anger of the green lobby. You are also under pressure to reduce industrial CO_2 emissions, but you have rejected these suggestions since the cost of implementing them would make British industry uncompetitive.

3 VOLCANOES AND CLIMATE CHANGE

Study Table 1.1 (page 23). This shows the major volcanic eruptions that have taken place between 1680 and 1970. Lamb's Dust Veil Index (DVI) is shown against each individual eruption. The index is a measure of the amount of ash injected into the atmosphere and, by inference, it is a measure of the likely effect that each eruption had on global cooling. The reference value of 1000 was chosen for the eruption of Krakatoa in 1883. The higher values indicate a greater likelihood that climate cooling took place.

i) Which eruptions had a DVI of 1000 or above?
ii) When did these eruptions take place?
iii) Calculate the total DVI values for each decade.
iv) Which decades had the lowest and highest total DVI values?

Study Figure 2.4b (page 38) which shows the pattern of temperature changes in the northern hemisphere during recent centuries.

i) Which decades were characterised by lower-than-average temperatures?
ii) How do these decades correspond with those characterised by high DVI values?
iii) Using the evidence from the exercises above, consider the relationships between the occurrence of volcanic activity and climate change.
iv) How might volcanic activity lead to global climate cooling?

Study Figure 2.4a which shows changes in the amount of acid deposited on the Greenland ice sheet over the last 1500 years. The amount of acid is thought to be representative of the amount of sulphate aerosols contained within the atmosphere. These aerosols are thought to be a product of volcanic activity.

i) Is there a relationship between Greenland ice core acidity and trends in northern hemisphere temperature changes?
ii) What are the most likely ways in which the sulphate aerosols are deposited on the Greenland ice sheet?
iii) Do the periods of cooling lag behind the changes in acidity?
iv) How would you interpret these changes?
v) Are there any time intervals when acid deposition was low?
vi) Do any of these time periods correspond with intervals of mild climate?

4 GLOBAL SEA-LEVEL RISE

Study Figure 1.15 (page 27). It shows sea-level rise values projected to 2100 AD.

i) Why should global sea-level rise take place due to temperature expansion?
ii) Why do the projected curves of future sea-level have large estimates of uncertainty associated with them?
iii) Suggest ways in which vertical movements of the land might influence the rate of relative sea-level change at individual locations?
iv) Choose a coastal area of interest. Try and obtain a 1:50 000 map of the area. Identify those areas likely to be flooded by a +10 m and +20 m rise in world sea-level.
v) Suggest *three* human consequences of such flooding.

◀ **Table 3.2** Global warming: role-play characters

SUGGESTED READING

Lamb, H. H. (1972) Climate: Present, Past and Future: Volume 1. Fundamentals and Climate Now. Methuen and Co., London.

Lamb, H. H. (1977) Climate: Present, Past and Future: Volume 2, Climatic History and the Future. Methuen and Co., London.

Lamb, H. H. (1982) Climate, History and the Modern World. Methuen and Co. Ltd.

Kemp, D. D. (1990) Global Environmental Issues: A Climatological Approach. Routledge, Chapman and Hall, London.

Intergovernmental Panel on Climate Change 1990 Scientific Assessment of Climate Change.

INDEX